Banned Books

BANNED BOOKS:

Informal Notes on Some Books Banned for Various Reasons at Various Times and in Various Places.

BY Mrs. ANNE (LYON) HAIGHT

New York

R. R. BOWKER COMPANY

1935

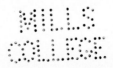

A List of Books
Compiled from an Exhibition
Held at The Junior League of the City of
New York, April 24, 1935

Printed in the United States of America

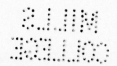

PREFACE

"**F**OR Bookes are not absolutely dead things, but do contain a potencie of life in them to be as active as that Soule whose progeny they are; nay, they do preserve as in a violl the purest efficacie and extraction of that living intellect that bread them. I know they are as lively and as vigorously productive as those fabulous Dragon's teeth; and being sown up and down, may chance to spring up armed men. And yet on the other hand, unless warinesse be used, as good almost kill a man as a good Booke; who destroys a good Booke, kills Reason itself; kills the image of God as it were in the eye." With these brave words from Milton's *Areopagitica* in mind, a small group from the New York Junior League Library set out last winter to discover whether censorship, in its various forms throughout the centuries, had indeed destroyed a good book, had indeed killed reason itself.

The results of the investigation were presented in concrete form in an exhibit of some two hundred famous books which had met the censor's ire. First to burn were Confucius' *Analects*, in 200 B.C., because Emperor Chi Huang Ti frowned upon all literature except "practical works" on alchemy, husbandry, medicine. Next came the suppression of Homer's epic poetry, in A.D. 35, because Caligula found Greek ideals of freedom inconvenient in Rome. Then came Dante, Virgil, and Propertius, these three, cast fanatically with carnival masks and frivolous gew-gaws into Savonarola's "Burnings of the Vanities" (just two years before the monk himself was burned at stake with all his works).

Down through the years the censor has waged a losing battle against the dangerous new ideas of

Preface

Galileo, Luther, Rousseau, Kant, Darwin, Marie Stopes; has fought in quixotic defence of purity against the windmills of Boccaccio, Casanova, Rabelais, Ibsen, Baudelaire, Joyce. And, with the returning surge of nationalism, Nazi Germany has hurled into its auto-da-fé such heterogeneous fuel as Remarque, Feuchtwanger, Upton Sinclair, Freud, Einstein, Jack London, and Marx. Almost as conglomerate is the Soviet blacklist which ranges from philosophic treatises, to *Huckleberry Finn*, and textbooks on Accounting. Fascist Italy is somewhat more consistent in that it bars any book containing "the seed of communism."

To generalize, an author is persecuted by one of three agencies—religious, political, moral—according as his offence is one of heresy, treason, or vice. Many of the authors presented distinguished themselves by falling under two categories, or even all three. Thus Abelard was persecuted in the twelfth century for his religious rationalizations, and in the twentieth for his too passionate love letters. Ernest Hemingway's fiction was banned by Fascist Italy for political tactlessness, but by Boston's Watch and Ward Society for moral impropriety.

We offer no panacea for the persecutions of authors and publishers, no solution to the problem of censorship. In the exhibition, and in this catalogue, the books speak for themselves. The data placed under each title is factual rather than editorial in nature: dates, circumstances of suppression, and quotations from contemporary comments. But the sum total of the investigation may serve as a springboard to a further consideration of the power of censorship.

ELISABETH LUCE MOORE
Chairman of The Library Committee,
New York Junior League.

New York, September, 1935.

A NOTE

THE actual editions banned were shown as far as possible in the exhibition, but when improcurable, later editions or substitutes had to be used. They have been arranged chronologically as to their first banning, as this method seems to give the best picture of the history of censorship. I have made exceptions in the arrangement where it seemed best not to separate authors of the same country, or those who were involved in the same movement or came under the same ban. I have not included in the catalogue all the material shown in the exhibition such as the pamphlets of Martin Luther. The intricate ramifications of his writings and of those of many other authors represented here would make complete catalogues in themselves and in many instances have already been published. Consequently I have only given an outline of some of the important facts and no collations, as it is really only the edition that is of interest. In checking the references I have sometimes found that the authorities differ and have selected the information which seemed most reliable.

The list of books refused admittance to this country, compiled in October, 1928, by the Post Office Department and the Custom House under the Treasury Department, has been of inestimable value. In April, 1929 a supplement was added that made a total of 739 titles. Of these, 379 were Spanish, 231 French, 5 Italian, 10 German, and 114 English. Many of these books should very decidedly be refused admittance, but it is of interest that many others are published in this country in school text-books and have been used here when practical.

A Note

Some countries today are more rigid in their censorship than others. The Irish Free State, for instance, issues a list almost weekly which is published in the trade journals. This explains the reason for a preponderance of material from such countries.

The Russian censorship is very complicated. A book suppressed under one leader of the government may be approved by another, and as there have been many changes since the revolution and not many authorities to rely upon, it has been a difficult subject to handle.

In explanation of "The Russian Censorship Terror" 1831–1853 under Nicholas I, referred to in this catalogue, I quote Dr. Yarmolinsky, Director of the Slavic Department of the New York Public Library "...panic stricken by the revolutions which swept Western Europe the authorities tightened the restrictions on the press so as to all but strangle it."

Unless designated, *Index* refers to the *Index Librorum Prohibitorum* of the Roman Catholic Church.

The basis of the material for this catalogue was assembled by a few members of the Library Committee of the Junior League of the City of New York. It is from this and from additional material that I have compiled this catalogue. As it is a catalogue of a specific exhibit, it may differ in detail when used in connection with similar exhibits given by other Junior Leagues.

The exhibit upon which this catalogue is based would not have been possible but for the courtesy of those who so kindly lent their books. Grateful acknowledgement is also made to those who accumulated the material and to those who gave their valuable assistance and advice. Their cöoperation was of inestimable value.

ANNE LYON HAIGHT.

September 19, 1935.

BANNED BOOKS

Informal Notes

HOMER. (c.1000 B.C.)
The Odyssey. Translated by T.E.Shaw.
Printed by Emery Walker, London, 1932.
387 B.C. Greece: Plato suggested expurgating Homer
for immature readers.
A.D. 35 Rome: Caligula tried to suppress *The Odyssey*
because it expressed Greek ideals of freedom—
dangerous in autocratic Rome.

CONFUCIUS. (551–478 B.C.)
Analects. (Annals of Lu, his native state, for 242
years, from 722 to 481 B.C.)
(In Chinese. Published in China.)
c.250 B.C. China: The first ruler of the dynasty of
Ts'in, wishing to abolish the feudal system, consigned to the flames all books relating to the
teachings of Confusius; he also buried alive hun-
dreds of his disciples.
c.200 B.C. The Emperor Chi Huang Ti ordered the
Analects and all other extant books, except practical works on medicine, divination, and husbandry, to be burned.

OVID, PUBLIUS. (43 B.C.–A.D. c.17)
Art of Love and other Poems, ed. by J.H.Mozley; the
Heroides and *Amores,* ed. by Grant Showerman; and
Metamorphoses, ed. by F.J.Miller. (Both Latin and
English. 2 VOLS.)
Loeb Classical Library. Harvard University Press.

Informal Notes

A.D.1 Rome: The Emperor Augustus banished Ovid for writing *Ars Amatoria* and for an unknown act of folly. He was sent to the Greek town of Tomi, near the mouth of the Danube, where he died in exile eight years later.

1497 Rome: The works of Ovid were cast, with those of Dante and his friend Propertius, into the great bonfire of Savonarola, as erotic, impious, and tending to corrupt.

1599 England: *Certaine of Ovids Elegies* (c.1597), translated by Christopher Marlowe, were burned in Stationer's Hall by order of the Archbishop of Canterbury, because of immoral tendencies.

1928 United States: The Customs still barred *Ars Amatoria*, although inexpensive editions were sold freely within the barrier.

1929 San Francisco: *Ars Amatoria* banned.

THE BIBLE: *The Book of Ruth.*
Gutenberg. Mainz, 1456.
(42-line Bible, first printed, 1456)

553 A.D. Eastern Roman Empire Emperor Justinian issued a decree commanding exclusive use of the Greek and Latin versions of the Bible and forbidding the *Midrash*, but accepting the Hebrew exposition of the *Old Testament.*

1409 England: The Synod of Canterbury meeting at St. Paul's London issued a decree forbidding the translation of the Scripture from one tongue to another and that no one should read a translation later than that of John Wiclif under penalty of greater excommunication, unless special licence be obtained.

1525–6 England: *The New Testament* translated by William Tyndale and printed on the Continent

4

On Banned Books

at Cologne and Worms was sent to England where it was violently suppressed by the Bishops and other clergy. Cardinal Wolsey ordered Tyndale to be seized at Worms, but he escaped to the protection of Philip of Hesse. The four editions printed on the Continent in the next four years were also suppressed.

1535 England: *The Old* and *New Testaments*, translated by Miles Coverdale, was the first complete Bible to be printed in English. Not being licensed by Church or State it had to be printed on the Continent just four hundred years ago.

1551 Spain: *The Inquisitorial Index of Valentia* (suppliment) forbade Bibles in Spanish or in any other vernacular.

1554 Spain: *The Inquisitorial Index of Valladolid* listed 103 editions of the Bible, condemned because of errors and heresies, to suppression, correction or cancellation.

1555 England: A proclamation by Queen Mary commanded "that no manner of persons, etc. presume to bring into this realm any M.S. books, papers, etc. in the name of Martin Luther, John Calvin, Miles Coverdale, Erasmus, William Tyndale, etc. or any like books containing false doctrine against the Catholic faith.

1560 Geneva: The Geneva or "Breeches Bible" went into 140 editions between 1560 and 1644, although it was not allowed to be used in the churches.

1624 Germany: The Bible translated by Martin Luther in 1534 which had been the most widely read book in the country was condemned to the flames by Papal authority.

1631 England: In the edition of 1000 copies of the Bible printed by R.Barker and assigns of Peter

Informal Notes

Bill the word "not" was omitted from the seventh commandment. The printers were heavily fined and the edition so vigorously suppressed that very few copies have survived. It was named "the Wicked Bible" by Henry Stevens.

1900 Rome: Pope Leo XIII decreed that translations of the Bible in the vernacular are permitted only if approved by the Holy See.

1926 Russia: *The Index of the Soviet Inquisition* states in their directions to libraries; "The section on Religion must contain solely anti-religious books. Religiously dogmatic books such as the Gospel, the Koran, the Talmud, etc. must be left in the large libraries, but removed from the smaller ones." It is said that the Bible is now refused admittance to the country.

1935 Scotland: A special licence for printing is still required for Bibles, Psalm and Prayer books.

ABÉLARD, PIERRE. (1079–1142)
Lettres d'Hélöise et d'Abélard.
Chez J.B.Fournier le jeune et Fils. De L'Imprimerie de Didot le jeune. Paris, 1796.

1120 France-Soissons: A provincial synod charged Abelard with religious heresy, forced him to burn his *Introductio ad Theologian*, and imprisoned him in the convent of St. Médard.

1140 Rome: All works banned by the Council at Sens and ordered burned by Pope Innocent III. St. Bernard called Abélard "an infernal dragon and the precursor of the anti-Christ."

1559 & 1564 Rome: All writings placed on the *Index*.

1930 United States: Custom's ban lifted on *Love Letters*.

On Banned Books

BACON, ROGER. (c.1214–c.1292)
Ordinis Minorum Opus Majus ad Clementem Quartum Pontificem Romanum.
Typis Gulielmi Bowyer, London, 1733. (written, 1268)

1257 England: Bonaventura, General of the Franciscan order, suspicious of Bacon's supposed dealings in the black arts, interdicted his lectures at Oxford, and placed him under the superintendence of the order in Paris. Here he remained for ten years, suffering great privations, and forbidden to write for publication.

1268 Oxford: *Opus Majus*, his most important work, *Opus Minus* and *Opus Tertium* were written at the request of Pope Clement IV.

1278 After the death of his protector, Clement IV, his books were condemned by Jerome de Ascoli, General of the Franciscans, afterwards Pope Nicholas IV, and Bacon was put into prison for fourteen years.

DANTE ALIGHIERI. (1265–1321)
La Divina Commedia.
Per Niccolò di Lorenzo. Firenze, 1481.
(first printed, 1472)

1318 France-Lombardy: *De Monarchia* was publicly burned.

1497 Italy-Florence: Works burned by Savonarola in the bonfire of the vanities.

1581 Portugal-Lisbon: *La Divina Commedia* prohibited by Church authorities until all copies were delivered to the Inquisition for correction.

1559 Rome: *De Monarchia* banned by Pope Paul IV and the *Index of Trent*.

1564 *De Monarchia* banned by the *Index of Trent*.

Informal Notes

SAVONAROLA, GIROLAMO. (1452–1498)

Compendium Totius Philosophiae.

Apud Iuntas. Venetiis, 1542.   (first edition, 1534)

1497 Italy: Savonarola transformed the pleasure loving Florentines into ascetics; and celebrated the annual carnival by the famous burning of the vanities, including works by Ovid, Propertius, Dante and Boccaccio.

1498 He was forced by tortures on the rack to confess his heresy in demanding church reforms, and in denouncing papal corruptions. After the ceremonial of degradation, he was hung on a cross and burned with all his writings, sermons, essays and pamphlets.

BOCCACCIO, GIOVANNI. (1313–1375)

Il Decamerone.

Nella Stamperia de i Giunti. Firenze, 1573.

(written, 1353)

1497 Italy-Florence: Manuscripts and printed parts were thrown into Savonarola's "bonfire of the vanities."

1559 Rome: Prohibited by the *Index* of Pope Paul IV, unless expurgated. The revisers retained the episodes; but transformed the erring nuns into noble women, the lascivious monks into conjurors, the Abbess into a Countess (21st. story), the Archangel Gabriel into the "King of the Fairies;" and the Pope authorized the edition.

c.1600 France: Censured by the Sorbonne and condemned by Parliament.

1922 United States: The Post Office authorities of Cincinnati seized an expurgated edition, and the district judge fined the bookseller $1,000.

1926 Banned by the Treasury Department.

On Banned Books

1931 Ban lifted by the Customs.

1932 Minnesota: Ban lifted.

1934 Detroit: Seized by the police as salacious.

1935 Boston: Still banned by the New England Watch and Ward Society.

Il Decamerone.

Ashendene Press. London, 1921.

1927 United States: The Customs Department mutilated a copy of this book, and returned it to Maggs Bros., London, with the text missing. C.H.St.John Hornby wrote a protest to the *London Times*.

SCHEDEL, HARTMANN. (1410–1485)
Nuremberg Chronicle.
Woodcuts by Wolgemut and Pleydenwurff.
Anton Koberger. Nuremberg, 1493.   (first edition)

1493 Nuremberg: This lavishly illustrated history of the world (beginning with the Creation) includes (leaf CLXIX, verso) a picture of the mythical female Pope Joan (with her baby!), here said to have succeeded as "John VIII" on the death of Leo IV (who died in 855). She is here said further to have been of English origin, though born in Mainz; to have disguised herself as a man, and gone to Athens with a learned lover; and later in Rome to have become so famous for knowledge of the Scriptures and for ability in public lectures and in learned discussions that she was finally elected Pope by general consent; and seemed to justify this choice until, during a procession to the Lateran Basilica, she suddenly broke down, gave birth to a son, and died ignominiously. The earliest known mention of her is by Stephen de

Bourbon who died in 1261. In 1400 an image of her (from the shoulders up, like the others) was included among the similar images of most of the (other!) Popes in Sienne Cathedral (in May 1600, at the request of Pope Clement VI, her name was changed to that of Pope Zachary), and in 1493 the legend was generally believed, but the earlier doubts became much more general, and the picture and account of Joan were piously inked over or cut out of very many copies of this and other books. In 1863 Döllinger at last proved the whole story to be wholly without any foundation in fact.

AGRIPPA, HENRY CORNELIUS. (1486–1535)
De Incertitudine et Vanitate Scientiarum et Artium.
Antwerp, 1530.   (first edition)
1509 Dôle: Charged with heresy for his lectures at the University, Agrippa was forced to take refuge with Maximilian in the Netherlands.
1531 Netherlands: *De Incertitudine*, a sarcastic attack on existing sciences and on the pretensions of learned men, was banned as heretical.
Belgium: The author was imprisoned at Brussels for satires written on the scholasticism of the professors.
1533 Rome: Charges of magic and conjury were brought against the author by the Inquisition for *De occulta Philosophia.* BOOK I. published, 1531.

MALORY, SIR THOMAS. (fl.1470)
The Birth, Life and Acts of King Arthur and his Noble Knights of the Round Table.
Embellished with many original designs by Aubrey Beardsley.

On Banned Books

J.M.Dent & Co. London, 1893–4. 2 VOLS.

(first printed by Caxton, 1485)

XVI Century, England: Roger Ascham denounced
the compilation of the Arthurian legend in *Morte
d'Arthur* as no more than "bold adultery and
wilful murder."

ERASMUS, DESIDERIUS. (c.1466–1536)
De Conscribendis Epistolis Opus.
Apud Theobaldum Paganum. Lugduni, 1557.

(first edition)

1512 England: *Encomium Moriae* (Praise of Folly), in
which kings, bishops, popes, and all manner of
people, were impiously shown to be subject to
folly, delighted the Pope, but was prohibited in
the Universities of Paris, Louvain, Oxford and
Cambridge. It was written in the house of
Thomas More.

1516 Switzerland-Basel: Erasmus dedicated his most
important work, the *Greek Testament*, to Pope
Leo X who lauded him for "exceptional service
to the study of sacred theology and to the main-
tenance of the true faith."

England: His powerful Catholic friends, including Cardinal Wolsey, Charles V, and Henry VIII,
urged Erasmus to declare against Luther. He
refused, but engaged in a sharp argument with
the reformers, and continued to attack the abuses
of the church, while remaining loyally within its
folds. While Erasmus continued to look at the
religious question in a sane, rational and objec-
tive way, the Lutherans and Calvinists calum-
niated him as a traitor to their cause, and Rome
denounced him for heresy.

1524 France-Paris: The Sorbonne forbad the sale or perusal of *Colloquies*.

1550 Spain: The *Index* condemned *Opera Omnia*.

1555 Scotland: Mary, Queen of Scots, forbad the reading of Erasmus.

1557 Rome: *De Conscribendis Epistolis Opus* forced to be corrected to conform with the Inquisition. On page 181, Erasmus crossed out all but six words.

1576 Pope Gregory XIII authorized an expurgated edition, published anonymously.

1612 *Spanish Index* of Sandoval devoted 59 folio pages in double columns to listing corrections to be made in his writings.

1930 Rome: Erasmus was not specifically mentioned in the latest edition of the *Index*.

LUTHER, MARTIN. (1483–1546)
Biblia.
Bremer Press. München, 1926. (first printed, 1534).

1519 Germany-Wittenberg: Luther nailed 95 theses, discussing the true meaning of Indulgences, to the Castle Church door connected with the University. The Theological faculties of Louvain and Cologne ordered copies of them to be burned on grounds of heresy.

1521 France: The Theological faculties of the University of Paris ordered the *Theses* burned.

1521 Rome: A Papal Bull by Leo X excommunicated Luther, and forbade printing, selling, reading, or quoting, his *Opera Omnia*, thereby creating a passionate interest in them. He also ordered a formal burning of Luther's effigy and books.
In three months 4000 copies of *Address to the*

German Nobility, in which he stated the causes of social discontent, were sold.

In five days 5000 copies of the vernacular edition of the *New Testament* were sold.

1521 Germany: Charles V, on his own authority, issued an edict against Luther, and ordered his books seized. At the same time he sent him a safe conduct to appear before the diet of Worms. The diet issued an edict against him, and threatened to exterminate his followers.

Strassburg: A contemporary comment was: "Lutheran books are for sale in the marketplace immediately beneath the edicts of the Emperor and the Pope who declared them to be prohibited."

1525 Luther became the virtual leader of the German nation.

He invoked a censorship of the "pernitious doctrines" of Anabaptists, Calvin and Zwingli.

1532 Luther turned the tables and demanded the suppression of the translation of the *New Testament* by Einser, a Catholic Priest.

TYNDALE, WILLIAM. (c.1492–1536)
The New Testament Of Our Lord And Saviour Jesus Christ.
Introduction by Francis Fry. (His copy on vellum)
Printed for Francis Fry. Bristol, 1864.

(first edition Worms, 1526)

1525-6 England: The English translation was the first printed book banned in England. The Ecclesiastical authorities damned it as "pernicious merchandise," and suppressed the first edition so energetically that only one copy has survived. It is in the library of the Baptist College in

13

Bristol. There is an incomplete copy in St. Paul's Cathedral, London.

1530 Marburg: Church and State authorities banned *Practyse of Prelates*, a treatise condemning the Catholic clergy and the divorce of Henry VIII.

1535 Belgium-Vilvorde Castle: Tyndale was imprisoned and burned at the stake with his books.

1546 England: Tyndale's books were ordered delivered to the Archbishop to be burned, because he had called church functionaries "horse-leeches, maggots, and caterpillers, in a kingdom."

1555 His books fell under the ban of Queen Mary's proclamation, and were forbidden in the realm for containing false doctrines against the Catholic faith.

THE KORAN. VII CENTURY.
Parchment Scroll. Illuminated. n.d.

1542 Switzerland: The Protestant authorities at Basel confiscated the entire edition published by Oporinus who promptly appealed to the scholars. Exonerated, by Luther, the edition was released.

1790 Spain: Ban lifted by the *Index.* Every version had been prohibited, especially the XII Century Latin translation by Peter of Cluny "cum refutationibus variorum."

1926 Russia: Restricted to students of history.

CALVIN, JOHN. (1509–1564)
Institutes of the Christian Religion.
(Translated from the original Latin.)
Presbyterian Board. n.d.

1542 France: *Civil and Canonical Law* forbidden by the Sorbonne.

1555 England: Queen Mary's proclamation required

14

"that no manner of persons presume to bring in-
to this realm any mss., books, papers, by John
Calvin . . . containing false doctrine against the
Catholic faith."

1559 & 1564 Rome: All works forbidden by the *Index*.

SERVETUS, MICHAEL. (VILLANOVANUS
MICHAEL) (1511–1563)
*Claudii Ptolomaei Alexandrini Geographicae Enarrat-
iones Libri Octo.*
Melchior & Caspar Trechsel. Lyons, 1535.

(first edition)

1553 France: The author's theological tracts, recast
as *Christianismi Restitutio*, were secretly printed
at Vienne, in Dauphiné, France, by Balthazar
Arnoullet, without name of place or printer. Soon
a letter from Geneva to the French authorities
denounced Servetus as a heretic and Calvin fur-
nished a sample of his handwriting to provehis
authorship, for only the initials M.S.V. appeared
at the end of the book, (though the name Servetus was on p.199). Under the auspices of the
Inquisitor-General of Lyons, Matthieu Ory (the
"Doribus" of Rabelais) Servetus was tried at
Vienne, found guilty and imprisoned, but was
allowed to escape, probably because he was a
friend of Pierre Paulmier, Archbishop of Vienne
and Primate of France. While waiting in Geneva
for a boat he went to church, was recognized and
imprisoned. After an incredibly unfair trial
(Aug. 14–Oct. 26) Servetus was, mainly as a re-
sult of Calvin's vindictiveness, condemned and
burnt at the stake with his books. Servetus
denied the tri-personality of the Godhead and the
eternity of the Son, but was passionately devoted

15

to the person of Christ and intensely sincere in his religious beliefs. Calvin's unfair book, 1554, vainly attempting to justify the burning of Servetus, seriously misrepresented the opinions of the latter, expressed at his trial, and in his books which had been destroyed as far as possible by Calvin himself. Calvin's charge that Servetus had attacked the authority of Moses and of the Bible in his edition of *Ptolomy's Geography* was unfair and absurd. Servetus had omitted the few words in question from his second edition (1541) and they had appeared in his first edition because the publisher had retained them from the 1525 edition of this translation (following here that of 1522) by Lorenz Friese who had attempted to reproduce in Latin the regular German term for the "Promised Land", "das gelobte land" (from "geloben" to promise) as meaning also "praised" (from "loben") stating that travelers however agree that it scarcely deserves to be "praised". Thus Calvin most unfairly converted a "geographical observation" by Friese into an alleged "theological error" by Servetus, as a special reason for having the latter burned to death.

RABELAIS, FRANÇOIS. (c.1494–1553)
Gargantua Adaptation de Gilles Robertet.
Image par Pierre Courcelles.
Maison Alfred Mame & Fils.
                    (first complete edition, 1564)
1533 France: The first two parts of *Pantagruel*, published without the knowledge of the author, were listed on the *Index* of the Sorbonne, and on the official black list of Parliament.

1535 Rome: A Papal Bull absolved Rabelais from ecclesiastical censure.

1546 France: The third book of *Pantagruel* was published under the author's name "avec privilège du Roi."

1552 Taking advantage of the King's absence from Paris, the divines of the Sorbonne censored the fourth book on publication.

1554 Cardinal de Chatillion persuaded Henry II to raise the ban on the works of Rabelais.

1564 Rome: The *Index* listed Rabelais as "Rebelisius" in its severe first class.

c.1900 France: An imaginative Frenchman, Robertet, refined the course language of these books in an adaption for children. The story of Pantagruel the giant, son of Gargantua the giant, their feasts, their wars, and adventures, told with a satiric humor had the same appeal to the imagination as Swift's *Gulliver's Travels*.

1930 United States: The Customs Department lifted the ban on all editions with the exception of those with so-called obscene illustrations, specifically Frank C. Pape's drawings for an Urquhart and Monteaux edition.

MACHIAVELLI, NICOLÒ. (1469–1527)
The Prince. Translated by E. Dacres.
R.Bishop for W.Hils. London, 1640.

(completed, 1513)

1555 Rome: Although Machiavelli had been the ambassador and advisor of Popes and Cardinals in his day, Pope Paul IV placed his works in the severest catagory of the *Index*, and Clement VIII made a fresh prohibition of a Lausanne edition of his *Discorsi*.

Informal Notes

1576 France: Selected maxims from *The Prince*, translated into French, were attacked by the Hugenot Gentillet for its political views.

1602 England: The Elizabethans derived from Gentillet their idea of and hostility for *The Prince*.

1935 Italy: Machiavelli's dream came true. *The Prince* demonstrated disjointed Italy's need for an all-powerful dictator supported by a national army. Mussolini paid Machiavelli tribute by encouraging the distribution of *Il Principe* in thousands of cheap copies.

TASSO, TORQUATO. (1544–1595)
La Gerusalemme Liberata.
Erasmo Viotto. Parma, 1581.

(Written, 1574; published, 1581)

1595 France: Suppressed by Parliament as containing ideas subversive to the authority of kings. *Di Jerusalemme Conquistator*, written and published in 1592, was a revision excluding the suppressed material, and other changes.

MONTAIGNE, MICHEL de. (1533–1592)
Les Essays.
Par la Societé. Paris, 1725.

(first two books published, 1580, third book, 1588)

1595 France-Lyons: Certain sections of the unexpurgated edition were banned. (5th. chapter of 3rd. book etc.)

1676 Rome: Listed in the *Index*, where they remain today.

On Banned Books

HOLINSHED, RAPHAEL. (d.c.1580)
Chronicles of England, Scotland and Ireland.
Imprinted for George Bishop. London, 1577.

(first edition)

1587 England: Upon publication of the second edition, Queen Elizabeth's Privy Council ordered excised certain passages about the history of Ireland, which were offensive to her.

It was from this edition that Shakespeare drew material for *Macbeth*, *King Lear* and *Cymbeline*.

1723 Queen Elizabeth's excisions were published separately.

SHAKESPEARE, WILLIAM. (1564–1616)
The Tragedie of King Richard the Second.
Printed by W.W. for Mathew Law. London, 1608.

(fourth edition)

1597 England: The original edition contained a deposition scene of the King, and it so infuriated Queen Elizabeth that she ordered it eliminated from all copies. It was not reinserted until after her death in the edition of 1608. Elizabeth complained to Lambarde that the play had been acted forty times in street and houses 'for the encouragement of disaffection'.

1601 Sir Gilly Merrick paid players forty shillings to revive the play on the afternoon when the Earl of Essex sought to rouse London against the Queen.

1788 *King Lear* was prohibited on the English stage until 1820, probably out of respect to King George III's acknowledged insanity, when the

Informal Notes

royal duties were transferred to a Regent.

1815 Coleridge said: "Shakespeare's words are too indecent to be translated . . . His gentlefolk's talk is full of coarse allusions such as nowadays you could hear only in the meanest taverns."

1818 Thomas Bowdler M.D. published the *Family Shakespeare* omitting "those words and expressions which cannot with propriety be read aloud in the family." Bowdlerize thereupon became synonymous with expurgate.

1931 United States: *The Merchant of Venice* was eliminated from the high-school curricula of Buffalo and Manchester, New York. Jewish organizations believed that it fostered intolerance.

JONSON, BENJAMIN. (1573–1637)
The Works of
Printed by Will Stansby. London, 1616.

(first edition)

1608 England-London: Jonson was imprisoned for collaborating with Marston and Chapman in the comedy *Eastward Ho* which was derogatory to the Scots. Released by the intervention of powerful friends, a feast was given in celebration.

RALEIGH, SIR WALTER. (1552–1618)
The History of the World.
W.Stansby for W.Burre. London, 1614.

(first edition)

1614 England: Called in by James I "for divers exceptions, but especially for being too saucy in censuring Princes."

On Banned Books

GALILEO, GALILEI. (1564–1642)
Dialogo dei due Massimi Sistemi del Mondo Tolemaico
e.Copernicano.
Per Gioe: Batistav. Firenze, 1632.

(first edition, 1630)

1616 Rome: Galileo was reprimanded by Pope Paul
IV, and told not to "hold, teach or defend" the
condemned doctrine of Copernicus, whose theory
he had tried to reconcile with religion.

1632 *Dialogo dei due Massimi Sistemi del Mondo* was
banned by Pope Urban VIII for heresy and
breach of good faith. The author was examined
by the Inquisition, under threat of torture, and
sentenced to incarceration at the pleasure of the
Tribunal. By way of penance he was enjoined to
recite once a week for three years the seven
penitential psalms.

1642 On Galileo's death, his wife submitted his manuscripts on telescopic and pendulum inventions to
her confessor who subsequently destroyed them
as heretical.

CERVANTES, SAAVEDRA MIGUEL de. (1547–
1616)
The Life and Exploits of the Ingenius Gentleman Don
Quixote De La Mancha.
Printed for William Miller. London, 1801.

(first part, 1605—second part, 1615)

1624 Portugal-Lisbon: a few paragraphs were proscribed by the Spanish *Index.*

1640 Spain-Madrid: Placed on the *Index* for one
sentence: "Works of charity negligently performed are of no worth."

Informal Notes

DESCARTES, RENÉ. (1596–1650)

Meditations.

Elzevir. Amsterdam, 1642.

(first edition, Paris, 1641)

1633 Holland: Descartes, a devout Catholic, abandoned his treatise on Copernican beliefs when he learned that Galileo's treatise had been suppressed, in Rome, for supporting Copernicus's hypothesis of the earth revolving around the sun. Rome: Through the influence of the Jesuits, this author's works containing Cartesian theories were placed on the *Index*, and forbidden in many institutions of learning until corrected or expurgated.

1665 Rome: *Meditations* was placed on the *Index* until corrected, as the whole system was opposed to the whole system of Aristotle.

1772 Rome: This edition was forbidden by the *Index*, unconditionally, probably because it contained matter written by others.

1926 Russia: All philosophic works suppressed.

1930 Rome: *Meditations* and six other books still remain on the *Index*.

PRYNNE, WILLIAM. (1600–1669)

Histrio-Mastix. The Player's Scourge, or, Actors Tragedie.

Printed for E.A. and W.I. for Michael Sparke. London, 1633. (first edition)

1633 London: This book, written with purity of conviction, and moral earnestness, was brought to the attention of the King and Queen by Archbishop Laud. Prynne violently denounced all theatrical plays, including those at court where they were frequently given, and he was therefore accused of a supposed attack on the Queen, who was fond of the drama. In consequence the Star Chamber decreed that he be fined, imprisoned, branded, and have his ears cut off. Later when Laud was on trial for alleged offences, and was sentenced to death, Prynne was one of the chief prosecutors.

BACON, FRANCIS, BARON of VERULAM and VICOUNT ST. ALBANS. (1561–1626)
The Essayes or Counsels, Civill and Morall.
Printed by John Haviland for Hanna Barret and Richard Whitaker. London, 1625.

(first complete edition)

1640 Spain: All works banned by the Inquisition and placed on Sotomayor's *Index.*

1668 Rome: Book IX, of *Advancement of Learning,* published in 1605, and dedicated to the King, was placed on the *Index, donec corrigetur.*

1707 Spain: All works condemned by the *Index.*

BROWNE, SIR THOMAS. (1605–1682)
Religio Medici.
Printed by E.Cotes for Andrew Crook. London, 1656.

(first edition, 1642)

1642 England: This famous work written as a "private exercise to myself" was printed without the knowledge of the author.

1645 Rome: The Latin translation was placed on the *Index,* although Browne professed to be absolutely free from heretical opinions. He insisted upon his right to be guided by his own reason when no specific guidance was proffered by Church or Scripture.

Informal Notes

MILTON, JOHN. (1608–1674)
Areopagitica, A Speech for the Liberty of Unlicenc'd Printing, to the Parliament of England.
(John Milton). London, 1644.   (first edition)
[Corrected by Arber's accurate reprint (1925 ed.)]

1644 England: This famed and eloquent plea for freedom of the pen was condemned by Cromwell and the Parliament of Protestant England for such sentences as these: "For Books are not absolutely dead things, but doe contain a potencie of life in them to be as active as that soule was whose progeny they are; nay, they do preserve as in a violl the purest efficacie and extraction of that living intellect that bred them. I know they are as lively, and as vigorously productive, as those fabulous Dragon's teeth; and being sown up and down, may chance to spring up armed men. And yet on the other hand unless warinesse be used, as good almost kill a Man as Kill a good Book; who kills a man kills a reasonable creature, God's Image, but he . . . who distroys a good Booke, kills reason itselfe, kills the Image of God as it were in the eye."

1652 France: *Pro Populo Anglicano Defensio*, written, in 1651, as a reply to the attack on the commonwealth by Salmasius, was burned for political reasons.

1660 England: *Pro Populo Anglicano Defensio* was publically burned. *Eikonoklastes*, first published in 1649, was burned by the common hangman at the time of the Restoration for attacking the hypocrisy of the religion of Charles II, and for arguing against the Divine Right of Kings. The author escaped the scaffold only through the influence of friends.

1694 Rome: *State Papers*, published posthumously and surreptitiously in 1676, were listed on the *Index*.

1758 *Paradise Lost*, translated into the Italian by Paolo Rolli, listed on the *Index*.

1930 *State Papers* still listed on the *Index*.

WILLIAMS, ROGER.
The Bloudy Tennent, Washed and Made White in the Bloud of our Lambe: Being Discussed and Discharged of Bloud-Guiltiness by Just Defence.
Printed by Mathew Symons for Hannah Allen. London, 1647.

1644 England: This book was ordered publicly burned by the House of Commons for the tolerating of all sorts of Religion.

1644 United States: Denying that state had authority over conscience and being outspoken in civil matters, Williams was "enlarged" out of Massachusettes to Rhode Island, where he bought land from the Indians.

PASCAL, BLAISE. (1623–1662)
Lettres à un Provincial.
Pierre de La Vallée (D.Elzevir). Cologne, 1657.
                    (first letter published anonymously, 1656,
                                and 17 others followed)
1657 France: Burned, for being too free with the dignity of all secular authorities.

1660 Latin edition burned by Parliament.

1789 Rome: *Pensées* placed on the *Index* "avec les notes de M. Voltaire."

1930 Both books have remained on the *Index*.

Informal Notes

MOLIÈRE, JEAN-BAPTISTE POQUELIN.
(1622–1673)

Tartuffe. (privelège du Roi, 1669)
L'Enseigne du Potcassé. Paris, 1928.

1664 France: *Tartuffe*, a satire on religious hypocrisy, banned from the public stage by Louis XIV who, nevertheless, read it aloud to an audience which included high dignitaries of the church. The first three acts were given repeatedly at court; but Molière could not get permission for a public performance. During these years the church called him "a demon in human flesh," closed his theatre, and tore down his posters.

1667 While the King was away in Flanders, the play was given as *The Impostor*. The theatre was ordered closed by the Chief of Police, and the Archbishop of Paris laid a ban of excommunication on all who might act in the play, read, or see it.

1669 Permission was granted by the King to perform the play in public.

VERGIL, POLYDORE. (c.1470–1555)

De Rerum Inventoribus.
Apud Danielem Elzevirium. Amsterodami, 1671.

(first printed, Venice, 1499)

1671 Rome: This work was placed on the *Index* because of a passage which suggests that the Church's doctrine of Purgatory stimulated a market for indulgences. The volume, treating of the origin of all things, ecclesiastical and lay, was so well liked that it was translated into French, German, English and Spanish.

1756 All editions appeared on the *Index*, except those following the text sanctioned by Pope Gregory XIII.

LA FONTAINE, JEAN DE. (1621–1695)
Contes et Nouvelles en Vers.
Amsterdam, 1762.   (PART I, 1665, PART II, 1666)
1675 France: Suppressed by the Lieutenant of Police in Paris for political satire.
1703 Rome: Placed on the *Index*.
1804 Again placed on the *Index*.

FÉNELON, FRANÇOIS DE SALIGNAC DE LA MOTHE. (1651–1715)
Les Aventures de Télémaque, Fils D'Ulysse. Imprimé Par Ordre Du Roi Pour L'Education de Monsieur Le Dauphin.
De L'Imprimérie de Didot L'Aine. Paris, 1783.
(first edition, 1699)
1697 Rome: Although the author had been appointed Archbishop of Cambrai four years earlier, his *Explications des Maximes des Saints* was condemned by Pope Innocent XII as being against Christianity.
1699 France-Paris: Mme. de Maintenon caused the author's banishment, pretending to believe *Télémaque* a satire on herself and the King. Actually she was punishing him for opposing her marriage to Louis XIV.

LOCKE, JOHN. (1632–1704)
An Essay Concerning Humane Understanding.
Printed for Thomas Basset. London, 1690.
(first edition)
1683 England: Locke's theory of civil, religious, and

philosophical liberty was too radical, and he escaped to Holland, the asylum of exiles, such as Decartes, Erasmus, Grotius, and Spinoza, in search of liberty of thought. There he hid for some time under the name of Dr. Van der Linden. King Charles II deprived him of his studentship at Oxford, thereby closing the University to him.

1700 Rome: The French translation of *An Essay Concerning Humane Understanding* was placed on the *Index* where it remains today.

1701 London: The Latin version was prohibited at Oxford with the express ruling "that no tutors were to read with their students this essential investigation into the basis of knowledge."

DEFOE, DANIEL. (1660?–1731)
The Life and Strange Surprizing Adventures of Robinson Crusoe, of York, Mariner:
Printed for W.Taylor. London, 1719.   (first edition)

1703 England-London: *The Shortest Way With the Dissenters*, 1702, a satire recommending that all dissenters be killed, was at first taken seriously by the Church Party. When the sarcastic import was discovered the book was burned and the author was fined, imprisoned and pilloried.

1720 Spain: *Robinson Crusoe* placed on the *Spanish Index*.

1743 Rome: *The Political History of the Devil* was listed and is now on the *Index*.

SWIFT, JONATHAN. (1667–1745)
A Tale of a Tub Written for the Universal Improvement of Mankind.
To Which is Added an Account of a Battel Between

28

the Ancient and Modern Books in St. James's Library. London, 1711.   (first edition, 1704)

1708 Ireland: *The Predictions for the Ensuing Year by Isaac Bickerstaff*, published in 1708, was burned as "such uncanny prescience could not otherwise than signify collusion with the evil one himself."

1726 Ireland: *Gulliver's Travels*, a satire on courts, political parties, and statesmen, was denounced on all sides as wicked and obscene.

1734 Rome: *A Tale of a Tub*, charged with ridicule of papists and dissenters, was listed on the *Index*.

1841 Listed in the catalogue of Pope Gregory XVI.

1881 Ban lifted by Pope Leo XIII.

VOLTAIRE, FRANCOIS MARIE AROUET DE.
(1694–1778)
Candide.
Illustrated by Rockwell Kent.
Random House. New York, 1929.
                               (first edition, 1758)

1716 France: The author was exiled to Tulle, and later to Sully, for composing lampoons against the Regent, Orleans.

1717 The author thrown into the Bastile for writing *Puero Regnate*, and *J'ai Vue*, libels against Louis XIV.

1734 *Lettres Philosophiques Sur les Anglais*, condemned and burnt by the Government.

1734 *Temple du Goût*, a satire on contemporary French literature, was condemned. Copies were seized and burnt, and a warrant issued against the author, who was not to be found.

1752 Prussia: *Diatribe du Docteur Akakia*, a most clever lampoon against Maupertuis, President of the Berlin Academy, caused the author to be arrested, and copies of the book to be burnt. In consequence Voltaire ended his connection with the Court of Frederick the Great.

1754 Rome: *Histoire des Croisades*, placed on the *Index* where it remains today.

1759 France: *Cantique des Cantiques*, banned and placed on the *Index* where it still remains.

1764 France and Geneva: *Dictionnaire Philosophique*, banned.

1929 United States-Boston: *Candide* was seized on its way to a class in French literature at Harvard; but was admitted later in a new edition.

The Customs, after 170 years, discovered Voltaire and banned *Candide* as obscene, although it was being studied in college class rooms the world over as a literary masterpiece. The defence was prepared by two Harvard professors.

No one writer of the XVIII Century contributed so many books to the flames as Voltaire. Many of his books remain on the *Index* today.

1935 Soviet Russia: All philosophic works forbidden.

MONTESQUIEU, BARON CHARLES LOUIS.
(1689–1755)
L'Esprit des Lois.
Garnier. Paris, n.d. (completed, 1748)

1721 France: *Lettres Persanes*, a satire on the social, political, ecclesiastical, and literary follies of the day, was written and published anonymously in 1721. It so shocked Fleury that Montesquieu was not admitted to the Academy until seven years after publication.

Rome: *Lettres Persanes* listed on the *Index*.

1751 France: The Sorbonne planned but did not carry

out a regular censure of the author for denouncing the abuse of the French monarchical system in *l'Esprit des Lois*. It has been ranked as the greatest book of the eighteenth century in France. Rome: Prohibited by the church authorities, although not with the entire approval of the Pope.

ADDISON, JOSEPH. (1672–1719)
Remarks on Several Parts of Italy etc. In the Years 1701, 1702, 1703.
Printed by Jacob Tonson. London, 1705.
(first edition)

1729 Rome: Placed on the *Index* of Pope Benedict XIII.

1745 *Spectator Papers*, written in collaboration with Steele, was condemned by the *Index*, in a French version of extracts entitled, *"Le Spectateur, ou le Socrate Moderne."*

ZENGER, JOHN PETER. (c.1680–1746)
The New York Weekley Journal. Containing the freshest Advices, Foreign, and Domestic.
Monday, December 17, 1733. Numb. VII.
(facsimile of original copy)

1734 United States-New York: The first number of the *Weekly Journal* appeared Nov. 5, 1733. In the second number appeared an article on the liberty of the press. It was also used in many subsequent numbers. A committee was appointed in Oct. 1734 from the Assembly to investigate the charges of libel against Zenger. They found numbers 7, 47, 48, and 49, libelous, and ordered them to be burned. The author was arrested and put in prison. Indicted and tried, he was so ably defended by Andrew Hamilton that he was acquitted. His defense became the precedent cited in later trials and defenses of freedom of speech and press. The organization founded for Zenger's defense, called itself "The Sons of Liberty." It opposed the stamp act thirty years later, through circulation of inflammatory handbills and newspapers. Ironically, this organization is today the Tammany Society of New York.

SWEDENBORG, EMANUEL. (1688–1772)
Principia; or the First Principles of Natural Things.
New-Church Union. New York, n.d.
(first edition, 1731)
1738 Rome: Placed on the Index where it remains today.
1909 United States-Philadelphia: *Amor Conjugalis* was seized by the Post Office authorities on grounds of obscenity.
1930 Russia: All works banned.

FIELDING, HENRY. (1707–1754)
Pasquin, a Dramatick Satire.
Printed for J. Watts. London, 1736.   (first edition)
1736 England-London: The play, containing direct criticism of the political corruption of the Walpole era, was a great success; but the Lord Chamberlain refused to license any other plays by this author. He thereafter devoted himself to the practice of law, and wrote novels far more daring than his plays.

On Banned Books

RICHARDSON, SAMUEL. (1689-1761)
The History of Pamela: or, Virtue Rewarded.
Adorned with copper plates by T. Bewick after the
English edition.
Printed by Isaiah Thomas. Worcester, Massachusettes,
1794. (first Worcester edition; first English edition published anonymously, 1740)
1755 Rome: The French translation by Abbé Prevost
   was listed on the *Index.*
   England: This volume was abridged, not for
   moral reasons, but for length, and given as a reward of virtue to children who excelled in their
   lessons.
   Sir Walter Scott feared *Pamela* would rather
   "encourage a spirit of rash enterprise than vig-
   orous resistance."
   Charles Lamb pictured a young lad retreating
   from the book "hastily with a deep blush."

CASANOVA, GIOVANNI JACOPO de
SEINGALT. (1725-1798)
Mémoires: Écrites par lui-même.
Ernest Flammarion. Paris, n.d.
                  (published, Leipzig, 1826-38)
1820 Germany-Leipzig: The original manuscript was
   confined to the safe of the publisher, Brockhaus,
   and has never been published in unexpurgated
   form, although it is an invaluable record of manners and morals of the eighteenth century.
1931 United States: Customs ban lifted, except for
   editions containing risqué illustrations.
1933 Ireland: Banned.
1934 United States-Detroit: Seized by the police,
   for being lascivious and immoral.

Informal Notes

DUMAS fils, ALEXANDRE. (1824–1895)
La Dame aux Camélias.
L.Carteret. Paris, 1929.　　　　(written, 1848)
1850 London: The authorities permitted the performance as an opera, *Traviata;* but the translation of the text, as a libretto, was forbidden.
1852 France: After being forbidden on the Paris stage for three years, the play was produced through the efforts of Morny, the influential minister of Napoleon III.
1863 Rome: All love stories by him placed on the *Index,* where they still remain.

DIDEROT, DENIS. (1713–1784).
L'Encyclopédie.
Paris, 1766–1777.　　　　(published, 1751–1772)
1752 France: The first two volumes were suppressed by the King's Council for political and religious outspokenness.
1754 Louis XV issued a privilege for the continuation of the work.
1759 Although innocent of heresy against the state, this work was looked upon with suspicion and alarm by those who were afraid to hear the truth. Consequently, the Royal Privilege was withdrawn. The work, however, was continued surreptitiously.
Rome: The seven volumes published were condemned by the *Index.*
1804 The complete work was placed on the *Index,* where it remains today.

On Banned Books

ROUSSEAU, JEAN-JACQUES. (1712–1778)
D'Émile, ou De l'Éducation.
Marc-Michael Rey. Amsterdam, 1762.

(first edition)

1762 France: Condemned by the Parliament of Paris to be torn and burned at the foot of the great staircase; The Archbishop published a pastoral against the author, who went in exile to Geneva, his birthplace.

1763 Switzerland: Condemned by the Council of Geneva. Whereupon Rousseau renounced his citizenship, and attacked the Council, and the Geneva constitution, in *Lettres de la Montagne.*
Rome: Both books placed on the *Index,* where they remain today.

1766 Rome: *Du Contrat Social,* and *Lettre à Christophe de Beaumont, Archevêque de Paris,* were placed on the *Index,* where they still remain.

1806 *Julie, ou la Nouvelle Héloise,* published 1761, was placed on the *Index,* where it remains today.

1929 United States: *Conféssions,* published in 1770, was banned by the Customs Department as being injurious to public morals.

1935 Russia: All philosophic works forbidden.

BEAUMARCHAIS, PIERRE-AUGUSTIN
CARON DE. (1732–1799)
Les Oeuvres. VOL. I.
Collin. Paris, 1809. (first edition)

1774 France: *Mémoires* was condemned to flames by Parliament for criticising the state powers.

1775 For two years *Le Barbier de Séville* was forbidden to be played on the stage.

1781 *Le Mariage de Figaro* was suppressed by Louis XVI at court and in public performances on the ground of profound immorality. The author was imprisoned in St. Larare. Napoleon called it "revolution already in action".

1781 Beaumarchais was charged with treason against the Republic and his works were suppressed.

GOETHE, JOHANN WOLFGANG von.
(1749–1832)
Faust, ein Fragment
Leipzig, 1790.   (first published)

1776 Denmark: *Sorrows of Werther*, was prohibited under a strict censorship exercised by the Lutheran authorities.

1808 Germany-Berlin: The State authorities suppressed the production of *Faust*, until certain "dangerous passages" concerning freedom were deleted.

SCHILLER, JOHAN CHRISTOPH FRIEDRICH von. (1759–1805)
Die Räuber ein Schauspiel.
J.G.Gottasche. Buchhandlung, Tübingen, 1805.

(written, 1777–8; published, 1781)

1782 Germany: The Duke of Württemberg, annoyed with Schiller for running away from his medical post at Stuttgart to see his drama performed at Mannheim, put him under a fortnight's arrest, and forbad him to write any more "comedies," or to hold intercourse with anyone outside of Württemberg. The Duke was also irritated by a complaint from Switzerland of an uncomplimentary reference to Graubünden in *Die Raüber*. All the author's famous poetic dramas, poems, philosophical, and historical works were written after this.

On Banned Books
KANT, IMMANUEL. (1724–1804)
Philosophy.
Printed by James Maclehose & Sons. Glasgow, 1879.

1792 Prussia: *Die Religion innerhalb der Grenzen der blossen Vernunft*, second part, was suppressed by the strong, Lutheran Prussian State, because it was opposed to the literal doctrines of the Lutheran Church.

1793 Königsberg: Both parts were published, and Frederick William II promptly forbade the author to lecture or write on religion, not so much because of his religious unorthodoxy, as for his supposed sympathy with French revolutionary ideas.

1827 Rome: *Critique of Pure Reason*, in the Italian, was placed on the *Index*, where it still remains.

1928 Russia: All works banned.

CAGLIOSTRO, ALESSANDRO. (BALSAMO, GUISEPPE) (1743–1795)
Life. By W.Trowbridge.
Brentano's. New York, 1926.

1789 Rome: Cagliostro, alchemist and imposter, was imprisoned by the Inquisition for pamphlets advocating necromancy and astrology.

1789 Spain: *Mémoires Authentiques de Cagliostro*, placed on the *Index*.
Maçonnerie Égyptienne placed on the Spanish *Index* for encouraging superstition.

1795 San Leo: The author died in prison. His collection of books and instruments were publicly burned, including a manuscript which denounced the Inquisition as making the Christian religion godless and degrading.

GIBBON, EDWARD. (1737–1794)
The History of the Decline and Fall of the Roman Empire.
Printed for W.Strahan and T.Cadell. London, 1776–88. (first edition)

1783 Rome: The first volume, in Italian (1779), was placed on the *Index* because it contradicted much official church history. In his vindication, which refers to attacks, more by Protestants than by Catholics, he says: "I stand accused . . . for profanely depreciating the promised land . . . They seem to consider in the light of a reproach, the idea which I had given of Palestine, as a territory scarcely superior to Wales in extent and fertility; and they strangely convert a geographical observation into a theological error. When I recollect that the imputation of a similar error was employed by the implacable Calvin, to precipitate and to justify the execution of Servetus, I must applaud the felicity of the country, and of this age, which has disarmed, if it could not mollify, the fierceness of ecclesiastical criticism."

1826 England: An expurgated edition was published by Thomas Bowdler.

1930 Although still on the *Index*, it is used in many Catholic colleges.

JEFFERSON, THOMAS. (1743–1826)
A Summary View of the Rights of British America Set Forth in Some Resolutions Intended for the Inspection of the Present Delegates of the People of Virginia, now in Convention. By a Native, and Member of the House of Burgesses.
Printed by Clementina Rind. Williamsburg, 1774.
Reprinted for G.Kearsly. London, 1774.

1774 England: This pamphlet was printed by sympathetic friends, without Jefferson's knowledge, and says "Our emigration to this country gave England no more rights over us than the emigration of the Danes and the Saxons gave to the present authorities of their mother country over England." It contained material rejected by the Virginia Constitutional Convention. The Declaration of Independence is practically a transcript of this book. Popular in America, the British edition caused the proscription of Jefferson's name by the English House of Parliament.

1833 Russia: *Mélanges Politique et Philosophiques Extraits dés Mémoires et de la Correspondence de T. Jefferson*, was banned for political reasons.

BARLOW, JOEL. (1754–1812)
Advice to the Privileged Orders.
J.Johnson. London, 1792.   (published, 1791–95)
1792 England: Eulogized by Fox, on the floor of the House of Commons, whereupon the Pitt Ministry suppressed the work and proscribed the author.

PAINE, THOMAS. (1737–1809)
Political Writings.
George H.Evans. New York, 1835.
                    (first edition, London, 1819)
1792 England: Paine was indited for treason because of his views expressed in *The Rights of Man*, published in 1790–92. Pitt commented: "Tom Paine is quite in the right . . . but if I were to encourage his opinion we should have a bloody revolution." The government tried to suppress the work.

Informal Notes

1797 T.Williams was prosecuted for publishing *The Age of Reason*, 1793, and found guilty. It was a defence of Deism against Christianity and Atheism.

HUNH LING FEI.
The Refugee.
In Chinese. Published in China.

LOU CHIEN-nan.
The Struggle.
In Chinese. Published in China.

1644–1911 China: In the early part of the Manchu régime a number of Chinese scholars were made to suffer for their writings about the dynasty. This policy of suppression rose to its height during the years 1774–1788, when thousands of books were collected from all parts of the Empire, and were censored or destroyed outright. Altogether 2,320 works were listed for total, and 345 for partial suppression, or minor alteration. Of these, at least 477 have been preserved, and are scattered today in various collections in China, Japan, Europe, and the United States.

CHÉNIER, ANDRÉ DE. (1762–1794)
Poésies.
Renaissance du Livre. Paris, 1913.
(first collected edition, 1820)

1792 France: His political writings, including *Avis au Peuple Français*, 1790, and *Ode à Charlotte Corday*, 1792, were privately printed and publicly banned.

1794 While imprisoned in the Saint Lazare by the Committee of Public Safety, Chenier wrote *Iambes*, attacking the Convention (Revolutionary party in power), and *Jeune Captive*, a poem of despair. He was guillotined, on a false charge of conspiracy, three days before Robespierre.

BABEUF, FRANÇOIS NOEL. (GRACCHUS) (1760–1797)
Tribune du Peuple.

(only card shown—no copy is known)

1794 France-Paris: Father of revolutionary socialism, Barbeuf attacked, in his *Journal de la Liberté de la Presse*, later called, *Tribune du Peuple*, not only the fallen terrorists after the execution of Robespierre, but also the economic theories of the Directoire.

1795 No. 33 of the *Tribune* was burned in the Théâtre des Bergères, by the *jeunesse dorée*, foes of Jacobinism, as a cure for the economic disaster that followed the collapse of the vicious dole system.

1796 No. 40 of the *Tribune* rallied thousands of workmen under Babeuf's slogan "Nature has given to every man the right to the enjoyment of an equal share in all property."

1797 The author was arrested, tried, and executed, in spite of the efforts of his Jacobean friends to save him.

STAËL, MADAME ANNE L.G.NECKER de. (1766–1817)
De l'Allemagne.
Chez H.Nicolle, à la Librarie Stéreotype. Paris, 1814.

(first edition, 1810)

1807 Rome: *Corinne* listed on the *Index* for immorality.

Informal Notes

1810 France: Condemned by Napoleon as "not French" in its political philosophy. The author was exiled from the country. The condemnation was no doubt due to Napoleon's personal animosity for de Staël, and his fear of her ambitions, as her salon was largely devoted to organizing political intrigues against him. Her political views were alleged to be so contaminating that Mme. Récamier was exiled for frequenting her salon, since she was undoubtedly implicated as well.

RACINE, JEAN. (1639–1699)
Théâtre Complet.
Verdière. Paris, 1817.   (first edition)
c.1810 France: Under the imperial censorship of Napoleon, certain passages in *Atalie*, written in 1691, alluding to tyranny, were cancelled before a new edition was permitted.

SHELLEY, PERCY BYSSHE. (1792–1822)
Queen Mab, a Philosophical Poem.
[Printed for Percy Bysshe Shelley.] London, 1813.
                        (first edition)
1811 England: Shelley and his friend Hogg were dismissed from Oxford, as being mutineers against academic authority, for publishing *The Necessity of Atheism.*
1815 *Alastor* was rejected by a library on grounds of immorality.
1842 *Queen Mab*, privately printed because of its opinions on moral and religious matters, was prosecuted for blasphemy. The publisher was released upon giving up all copies in his possession.

On Banned Books

DARWIN, ERASMUS. (1731–1802)
Zoonomia.
J.Johnson. London, 1794–6.   (first edition)
1817 Rome: Placed on the *Index.*
   England: Studied in the schools.

STERNE, LAWRENCE. (Yorick) (1713–1768)
A Sentimental Journey Through France and Italie by Mr. Yorick.
Printed for T.Becket. London, 1768.   (first edition)
1819 Rome: The translation, by Ugo Foscolo, was listed on the *Index*, where it remains today.

GOLDSMITH, OLIVER. (1730–1774)
History of England.
J.Newbery. London, 1764.   (first edition)
1823 Rome: The Italian translation was listed on the *Index*, *"donec corrigetur".*
1930 *An abridged History of England from the Invasion of Julius Caesar to the Death of George II,* still remains on the *Index.*

ROSSETTI, DANTE GABRIEL. (1828–1882)
Verses
G.Polidori. London, 1847.   (first edition)
1833-46 Rome: Some of the author's poems, translated from the Italian, were placed on the *Index*, where they remain today.
1871 England: Robert Buchanan, under the pseudonym of "Thomas Maitland," in an article in the *Contemporary Review*, attacked Rossetti and the "Fleshly School of Poetry" as immoral, and one of his sonnets as, "one profuse sweat of animalism." Rossetti, deeply hurt, replied in an article called the *Stealthy School of Criticism.*

Informal Notes

ANDERSON, HANS CHRISTIAN. (1805–1875)
Aeventyr og Historier.
Gyldendatske Doghandel. Köbenhavn, 1925.
 (first fairy tales, Copenhagen, 1835)
1835 Russia: Banned, by Nicholas I, during the "Censorship Terror."
1849 Ban removed by Alexander II.
1935 It is said that the Soviet Government has discouraged fairy tales in the schools on the ground that they glorify princes and princesses.

HUGO, VICTOR MARIE. (1802–1885)
Oeuvres Complètes.
Renduel. Paris, 1819–1838.   (first edition)
1829 France: *Marion Delorme*, published in 1831, was prohibited by the official censors because Louis XIII was pictured as a "weak, superstitious and cruel prince," which might provoke public malevolence and lead to a disparagement of his Majesty, Charles X. Hugo appealed to the King. A royal veto sustained the prohibition; but Charles offered to raise the poet's pension from two to six thousand francs. After Charles was removed by the Revolution of 1830, the play was produced at the Thèâtre Français.
1830 *Hernani:* The Inspector General of Theatres ordered the correction of such passages in this play as, "Thinkest thou that kings to me have aught of sacredness?" A literary war ensued: Classicists and Romanticists fought nightly in the theatre and out. The Classicists hired professional claques. Théophile Gautier organized a troop of volunteers, "resolved to take their stand upon the rugged mount of Romanticism, and to valiantly defend its passes against the assault of

44

the Classics." In the end Romanticism tri-
umphed; but not without a martyr, for a young
man died fighting a duel over the play.

1832 *Le Roi S'Amuse:* Prohibited, after the first performance, by order of the Prime Minister
Quizot, for derogatory allusions to Louis-
Phillipe. It was produced fifty years later under
the supervision of the author.

1834 Rome: *Notre Dame de Paris*, published in 1831,
was placed on the *Index*, and is there today.

1850 Russia: All works banned by Nicholas I.

1853 France: Copies of *Napoleon le Petit* were seized
by the police. This satire was written one year
after the author began his twenty year exile for
criticizing the Government.

1864 Rome: *Les Misérables*, published two years
earlier, was listed on the *Index* where it remains
today.

GAUTIER, THÉOPHILE. (1811–1872)
Mademoiselle de Maupin.
L.Conquet. Paris, 1883.   (first edition, 1835)

1831–1853 Russia: Banned, by Tzar Nicholas I, during the period of "Censorship Terror."

1871 England: Robert Buchanan, always ready to
criticise, denounced the *Memoire of Charles
Baudelaire* as "skillfully and secretly poisoning
the mind of the unsuspicious reader."

1917 United States: The New York Society for the
Suppression of Vice noticed a copy of *Mlle. de
Maupin* in the window of McDermitt Wilson,
Booksellers. As it was opened at a "corrupting"
illustration, the booksellers were tried in court
and acquitted. Mr. Halsey of the bookshop sued
the Vice Society for damages, and finally won

the decision after it had been once reversed. The Society paid Halsey $2500, plus interest accruing throughout the year of the law's delay.

BLANC, JEAN JOSEPH CHARLES LOUIS. (1811–1882)
Organization du Travail. Association Universelle. Ouvriers. Chefs, D'Ateliers, Hommes de Lettres.
Administration de la Librairie. Paris, 1841.

      (first published in *Revue du Progrès,* 1839)
1839 France: The author tried to put into practise the principles of his work (abolition of competition, equalization of wages, immersion of personal interest in the common good) by establishing co-operatives financed by the state. The state initiated "National Workshops," a parody of Blanc's principles, involving a flat wage of two francs a day for cleaning the Gare Montparnasse, re-planting trees on the Boulevards, and digging up the Champ-de-Mars. Thousands of unemployed flocked to Paris. Blanc was held responsible for the disastrous consequences, and barely escaped to London. After he had left he was condemned to deportation, and his work suppressed until the fall of the Empire.
1840 Russia: All works banned for political reasons.

BALZAC, HONORÉ de. (1799–1850)
Les Contes Drôlatiques.
Illustrées de 425 Dessins par Gustave Doré.
John Camden Hotten, Londres, 1860.

      (commenced 1833—never finished)
1841 Rome: All works listed on the *Index.*
1850 Russia: All works banned.

1914 Canada: *Droll Stories* banned by the Customs and is still forbidden.

1930 United States: Custom's ban lifted on *Droll Stories*.

STENDHAL, HENRI BEYLE. (1783–1842)
Rouge et Noir.

Garnier. Paris, n.d.   (first edition, 1831)

1850 Russia: *Rouge et Noir*, and all other works, banned by Nicholas I.

BAUDELAIRE, CHARLES PIERRE. (1821–1867)
Fleurs du Mal.

Auguste Poulet Malassis. Paris, 1857. (first edition)

1857 France: The author, publisher, and printer, were prosecuted under the second Empire, for an "outrage aux bonnes moeurs." Baudelaire was arrested in the cemetery of Montparnasse, where he was peacefully reading Boswell's *Life of Johnson*, and fined 300 francs.

1866 Belgium-Brussels: The six poems, suppressed from *Les Fleurs du Mal*, were published under the title of *Les Épaves*, and were widely circulated in France.

Victor Hugo wrote to Baudelaire, "Vous dotez le ciel de l'art d'un rayon macabre, vous créez un frisson nouveau."

FLAUBERT, GUSTAVE. (1821–1880)
Madame Bovary, Moeurs de Province.

Imprimé pour la Société du Livre D'Art par L'Imprimerie National. Paris, 1912.   (first edition, 1856)

1857 France-Paris: The author was taken to court for "outrage aux bonnes moeurs," as depicted in *Madame Bovary*. He was acquitted on the ground that the passages cited by the prosecution, though reprehensible, were few in number compared with the extent of the whole work.

1864 Rome: *Madame Bovary* and *Salammbô* were placed on the *Index*, where they remain today.

1927 United States: The *Temptation of St. Anthony* was unsuccessfully attacked by the New York Society for the Suppression of Vice.

1935 This same Society attacked *November*, written before the author became of age, which he often debated publishing during his lifetime, but which awaited his death for publication in France, and was not translated into English until 1930. Magistrate Goldstein's decision: "The criterion of decency is fixed by time, place and geography and all the elements of a changing world. A practice regarded as decent in one period may be indecent in another."

MAUPASSANT, HENRI RENÉ ALBERT GUY
de. (1850–1893)
Une Vie, L'Humble Vérité.
Havard. Paris, 1883.   (first edition)

1880 France: Legal proceedings against *Des Vers* were withdrawn through the influence of Senator Cordier. Flaubert, the teacher of Maupassant, who had been prosecuted for *Madame Bovary*, congratulated his pupil on the similarity of their literary experiences.

1883 The sale of *Une Vie* was forbidden at railway bookstalls. The prohibition drew much attention to the master of the short story.

1930 Canada: Many of this author's works still remain on the black list.

On Banned Books

HEINE, HEINRICH. (1797–1856)
De l'Allemagne.

Levy. Paris, 1855.   (first edition, 1836)
1835 Germany: The Bund issued a decree forbidding
the publication of any writings by members of
the "Young Germany" coterie. In consequence,
Heine, being a member, went to Paris where he
could write freely. There he received an annual
income from the fund provided for political
refugees.
1836 Rome: *De la France, Reisebilder* and *De
l'Allemagne,* were placed on the *Index,* where
they remain today.
1844 *Neue Gedichte,* listed on the *Index,* where it still
remains.
1933 Germany: Works burned in the Nazi bonfires.
(Heine, although born a Jew, embraced Christianity in 1825.)

MARX, KARL. (1818–1883)
*Manifesto of the Communist Party: Bible of Soviet
Russia.*

Geneva, 1900.   (published in Russian)
*Capital, A Critique of Political Economy, The Process
of Capitalist Production.*

Charles H. Kerr and Company. Chicago, 1926.
                    (first edition, 1867)
1843 Prussia: *Rheinische Zeitung,* journal of advanced
political and social ideas, was suppressed one
year after Marx became editor.
c.1845 France: Marx was expelled at the instance of
the Prussian Foreign Office for contributing to
the radical magazine *Vorwärts* which was then
liquidated.
1849 Prussia: *Neue Rheinische Zeitung* submitted "an

49

organ of democracy," which advocated non-payment of taxes, and armed resistance against Emperor Frederick William. It was suspended, and the editor, Marx, was tried for treason. Although unanimously acquitted by a middle-class jury, he was expelled from the country. Being unwelcome in Paris, he retired to London for the rest of his life.

1878 After two attempts on the life of the aged Emperor William I, Bismark took the opportunity to persuade the Reichstag to enact stringent measures against the Social Democrats, and prohibited their literature, including the Manifesto.

1929 China: The Nationalist Government sent armies against the sporadic red outbreaks in the provinces, and stopped, where possible, the reading of the *Manifesto* and *Capital*.

THE LIBERATOR.
William Lloyd Garrison and Isaac Knapp, Publishers.
Boston, Massachusettes. Saturday, January 1, 1831.
VOL.I,NO.I

1831 United States: A Georgia Senate Resolution offered a reward of $5000 for the apprehension and conviction in Georgia courts of the editor or publisher "of a certain paper called *The Liberator*," because it was regarded as likely to cause unrest and trouble.

GOODRIDGE, REV. SAMUEL C. (1793–1860)
Peter Parley's Annual. A Christmas and New Year's Present for Young People.
Illustrated by George Cruikshank and Others.
Simpkin, Marshall and Company. London, 1843.
(pirated English edition)

1843 Russia: Prohibited unconditionally by Nicholas I.
United States: Goodridge, under the pseudonym
of Peter Parley, wrote about 170 tales, moral and
historical for children. Seven million volumes
were said to have been sold. They proved so
popular that various pirated editions were published in England, and illustrated by some of the
famous illustrators of the day, including Cruikshank, Leech and Phiz.

STOWE, HARRIET BEECHER. (1811–1896)
Uncle Tom's Cabin, or Life Among the Lowly.
John P. Jewett and Company. Boston, 1852.
(first edition)
1852 Russia: Banned under the "censorship terror"
of Nicholas I.
1855 Papal States: The sale of the volume was prohibited, though not listed on the *Index*.
1858 Russia: Ban lifted on the Russian translation.

HAWTHORNE, NATHANIEL. (1804–1864)
The Scarlet Letter, a Romance.
Ticknor and Fields. Boston, 1850.   (first edition)
1852 Russia: Banned by Nicholas I in the "censorship terror" until 1856.
United States: Rev. A.C. Coxe argued "against
any toleration to a popular and gifted writer
when he perpetrates bad morals—let this broker-
age of lust be put down at the very beginning."
1925 United States: The screen version was made to
comply with the demand of the Board of Censorship for the marriage of Hester.
1935 A bust of the author is in the Hall of Fame in
New York University.

WHITMAN, WALT. (1819–1892)

Leaves of Grass.

Brooklyn, 1855.   (first edition)

1855 United States: The Poems shocked American Puritanism and English Victorianism.

1860 The Secretary of the Interior discovered the "indecent book" and instantly discharged the author from the department. Fittingly enough, the Department of Justice promptly offered him a post.

1881 Boston: The District Attorney threatened criminal prosecution unless the volume was expurgated. The book was withdrawn; but published later in Philadelphia.

Whittier, in a rage of indignation, threw his first edition into the fire, although he himself had suffered persecution for his abolitionist poems.

Wendell Phillips' comment was "Here be all sorts of leaves except fig leaves."

A bust of Whitman is in the Hall of Fame in New York University.

WOODHULL, VICTORIA. (1836–1927)

Woodhull and Claflin's Weekly.

1872 United States: The November 2nd issue, containing an exposé of the private life of Pastor Henry Ward Beecher, was suppressed at the instance of Antony Comstock for obscenity and libel. The feminist editors were jailed.

On Banned Books

CLEMENS, SAMUEL LANGHORNE. (Mark
Twain) (1835–1910)
The Adventures of Tom Sawyer.
The American Publishing Company. Hartford, 1876.
(first edition)
1876 United States-Brooklyn: Excluded from the
children's room in the Public Library.
Denver: Excluded from the Public Library.
1930 Russia: Confiscated at the border.

Adventures of Hucklebury Finn.
Charles L.Webster and Company. New York, 1884.
(first edition)
1885 Concord, N.H.: In the home town of Henry
David Thoreau the book was banned by the
Public Library as "trash and suitable only for
the slums." The Concord Free Trade Club retaliated by electing the author to honorary
membership.
Brooklyn: Excluded from the children's room of
the Public Library.
NOTE: Mrs. Clemens censored the book and deleted the profanity and other strong passages,
but left some which have at times been criticized,
such as: "All kings is mostly rapscallions." CHAP.
23; and, "so the king be blatted along," CHAP. 25.
The London Athenaeum has called it one of the
six greatest books ever written in America.

THE BOOK OF COMMON PRAYER OF THE
CHURCH OF ENGLAND ADAPTED FOR GENERAL USE IN
OTHER PROTESTANT CHURCHES.
William Pickering. London, 1852.
1852 England: Though compiled by Prince Albert,
consort of Queen Victoria, and Chevalier Bunsen,

this *Liturgy* was suppressed when it was discovered that it did not contain the slightest reference to Christ as God.

MILL, JOHN STUART. (1806–1873)
Principles of Political Economy with some of their Applications to Social Philosophy.
Longmans, Green and Company. London, 1929.
(first edition, 1848)
1856 Rome: The *Index* listed this work which with Mill's *System of Logic*, epitomized the social and philosophical theories of the more educated English radicals of the day.

BROWNING, ELIZABETH BARRETT. (1806–1861)
Aurora Leigh.
Chapman and Hall. London, 1857.   (first edition)
1857 United States-Boston: Condemned as "the hysterical indeciencies of an erotic mind."
England: Thackery declined to publish *Lord Walter's Wife* because of the "immoral situation;" and it was excluded from the monopolistic Circulating Libraries.

ELIOT, GEORGE. (Mary Anne Evans). (1819–1880)
Adam Bede.
William Blackwood and Sons. Edinburgh and London, 1859.   (first edition)
1859 England: This book, although a popular success, was attacked as "the vile outpourings of a lewd woman's mind," and was soon withdrawn from the circulating libraries of the period.
1908 France: *Adam Bede* and *Mill on the Floss* were

listed by Abbé Bethléem as *"romans honnêtes,* and *Les Tribulations du Révèrend Barton* as *"delicieux a lire."*

SWINBURNE, ALGERNON CHARLES.
(1837–1909)
Poems and Ballads.
Edward Moxon and Company. London, 1866.

(first edition)

1860 England: *The Queen Mother* and *Rosamond* were withdrawn from circulation, because of strenuous objections to their licentiousness.

1866 *Poems and Ballads* was temporarily suppressed in a storm of excitement over the author, whom Robert Buchanan classed with Rossetti and his circle as "the Fleshly School."

1875 *The Devil's Due,* an open letter libeling Buchanan, was immediately suppressed.

MOORE, GEORGE. (1852–1933)
Flowers of Passion.
Provost and Company. London, 1878–(1877).

(first edition)

c.1878 Ireland: Edmund Yates called the author of *Flowers of Passion* a "bestial bard," and advised whipping him, and burning the book.

1883 England: *A Modern Lover,* a three volume novel, was banned by Mudie's Circulating Library which exercised a virtual censorship because every one borrowed, and few bought, the expensive three volume novels of the day. Moore vowed revenge and published his next novel, *A Mummer's Wife,* 1885, in an inexpensive single volume, thereby starting a vogue to break the monopoly of circulating libraries.

Informal Notes

1894 Circulating Libraries refused to stock *Esther Waters*.

1929 United States: The Customs refused admittance to *A Story Teller's Holiday*.

1932 The Customs Court judged it obscene.

1934 The Treasury Department admitted it as a modern classic.

EXTRACTS PRINCIPALLY FROM ENGLISH CLASSICS: Showing that the Legal Suppression of M.Zola's Novels Would Logically Involve the Bowdlerizing of some of the Greatest Works in English Literature.

[Compiled by and privately printed for Henry Vizetelly. 1820-94]

1888 England-London: This volume is in defence of Vizetelly, publisher and champion of Flaubert, Goncourt, Gautier, Maupassant, Daudet and Longfellow. Nevertheless, he was condemned to prison for publishing such "pernicious literature" as the novels of Zola.

ZOLA, ÉMILE. (1840–1902)

Nana. Complete and Unabridged.

Vizetelly. London, n.d. (first edition, France, 1880)

1888 England: Vizetelly, the publisher, was imprisoned for publishing the novels of Zola, although, ironically, it was the expurgated editions of Zola's novels that so outraged the Victorian era.

1894 Rome: *Opera omnia* placed on the *Index.*

1898 France: Zola caused a judicial inquiry to be made into the notorious *affaire Dreyfus* which was convulsing French politics and society, and published the open letter, *J'Accuse,* in *L'Aurore.*

On Banned Books

It was a strong denunciation of all who, on the slightest evidence, had convicted Dreyfus of selling military secrets, had banished him to Devil's Island, and had refused all appeals for a new trial. Zola, condemned for libel of the army chiefs, escaped to England, where the publisher of his "pernicious novels" had been jailed.

1929 Jugoslavia: All works banned.

HARDY, THOMAS. (1840–1928)
Tess of the D'Urbervilles: A Pure Woman Faithfully Portrayed.
Published by James R.Osgood, McIlvaine and Company. London, 1891.   (first edition)
c.1891 England: Banned by the Circulating Libraries which held a virtual censorship over bourgeois reading.
United States-Boston: Highly disapproved of.
1896 England: *Jude the Obscure* banned by the Circulating Libraries.

WILDE, OSCAR O'FLAHERTIE. (1856–1900)
Salomé.
Translated by Lord Alfred Douglas.
Pictured by Aubrey Beardsley. Elkin Mathews. London, 1894.   (first edition, Paris, 1893)
1892 England: The play was being rehearsed in London by Sarah Bernhardt when the Lord Chamberlain withheld the license on the ground that the play introduced biblical characters.
1895 France: Played by Sarah Bernhardt.
United States-Boston: Banned in book form.

Informal Notes

KIPLING, RUDYARD. (1865–)

A Fleet in Being: Notes of Two Trips With the Channel Squadron.

Macmillan and Co. London, 1898.   (first edition)

1898 England: Suppressed. The book was accused of betraying naval secrets, although the author was well known as an intense patriot.

TOLSTOI, LEO. (1828–1910)

The Church and the State.

Berlin, (1891) (in Russian)   (first edition)

1880 Russia: Various works forbidden publication were printed in Switzerland, England and Germany.

In his early days, the writings of Tolstoi were greatly influenced by the philosophy of Rousseau, especially as expressed in *Émile*.

1890 United States: *The Kreutzer Sonata* was forbidden by the Post Office Department. In the ensuing controversy Theodore Roosevelt denounced the author as a "sexual and moral pervert."

1926 Russia: Many ethical works banned.

Hungary: All works banned.

1929 Italy: All works banned except in expensive editions.

IBSEN, HENDRIK. (1828–1906)

Ghosts.

Everyman's Library. New York, 1935.

(first published, London, 1881)

1881 Norway: The play, being a diagnosis of the diseases of modern society, and intended as a reform, was received with a tumult of ill will.

1892 England: Application for license was refused by the Lord Chamberlain.

Long after Ibsen's position had been recognized in modern letters, the censor still interposed his shocked and obstinate personality between the British public and the great Norwegian author.

c.1915 Ban removed by the censor of plays.

1935 United States: Play may not be legally given on the stage.

P'EN HAN-NIEN.
Divorce.
(In Chinese. Published in China.)

KUO MO-JO.
My Youth.
(In Chinese. Published in China.)

1884 Placed on the Chinese Index.

The purpose of the Index was to suppress Communistic and revolutionary writings which denounce capitalism and aim at stimulating class struggle. Novels and essays are included, as well as serious studies. Although some of the books appear to have nothing of a revolutionary nature in them they are listed because they have been translated by a Communist.

D'ANNUNZIO, GABRIEL. (1863–)
The Triumph of Death.
Translated from the Italian by Georgina Harding.
William Heinemann. London, 1898.
(first Italian edition, 1894)

1911 Rome: All love stories and plays placed on the *Index.*

1898 United States-Boston: Brought to court by the Watch and Ward Society, but not convicted.

(cont.) While the author lives enshrined, by the Lake of Garda, as Italy's beloved patriot and poet, the Index further prohibited his mystic poetry and mystery plays.

SHAW, GEORGE BERNARD. (1856)
Plays: Pleasant and Unpleasant.
Brentano, New York, 1919.

            (first edition, London, 1898, 2 vols.)

1905 United States: The New York Public Library withdrew *Man and Superman* from the public shelves to reserve action. Shaw, infuriated, coined the word "Comstockery." Anthony Comstock retaliated, and took arms against "this Irish smut-dealer's books." *Mrs. Warren's Profession* was taken to court where it was held not actionable. The Comstock publicity greatly increased the attendance at the stage production; and police reserves were called out on the opening night to dispel the crowds.

1922 England: In London the Lord Chamberlain refused to license *Mrs. Warren's Profession* for production.

1929 Jugoslavia: All works banned from the public libraries.

1933 England: *The Adventures of the Black Girl in her Search for God* was banned by the Cambridge Public Library.

GILBERT, W.S. (1836–1911), and SULLIVAN, ARTHUR. (1842–1900)
The Mikado, Or the Town of Titipu.
Chappell and Company. London, 1900.

c.1905 England: The British Foreign Office was much distressed for, although first performed in 1885, and the operetta had been a great popular success, "The Lord Chamberlain suddenly awoke to the unsuspected dangers in the piece, and forbade its further production on the ground that it might give offense to our Japanese allies." As a matter of fact the music was being played by Japanese bands on Japanese ships in the Medway River during the prohibition of the play.

MAETERLINCK, MAURICE. (1862–)
Mona Vanna.
Translated by Alexis Irénée DuPont Coleman.
Harper and Brothers. New York, 1905.
                    (first edition, Brussels, 1902)
1909 England: Censored by the Lord Chamberlain as improper for the stage. He said "Our decision was almost universally upheld."
1914 Rome: *Opera Omnia* listed on the *Index*.

DIMNET, ABBE ERNEST. (1869–)
La Pensée Catholique dans L'Angleterre Contemporaine.
Le Coffre. Paris, 1905.   (first edition)
1907 Rome: Listed on the *Index*, where it remains today.

APPOLLINAIRE, GUILLAUME. (WITH FLEURET AND PERCEAU). (1880–1918)
L'Enfer de la Bibliothèque Nationale.
Mecure de France. Paris, 1913.   (first edition)
1913 France: The publication of this book is said to have caused one of the authors to lose his position in the Bibliothèque Nationale.

Informal Notes

FRANCE, JACQUES ANATOLE THIBAULT.
(1844–1924)
L'Île des Pingouins.
Celman Levy. Paris, 1908.   (first edition)
1922 Rome: The *Index* placed its most stringent pro-
hibition on the reading of the works of France by
listing simply and conclusively *Opera Omnia.*
Thus they remain in the latest edition of the
Index, (1930).

LOUŸS, PIERRE. (1870–1925)
Aphrodite; Ancient Manners in the English Version.
Prepared by Willis L. Parker. Profusely Illustrated.
Arden Book Company. New York, 1932.
                        (first French edition, 1896)
1929 United States: Banned by the Customs Department as lascivious, corrupting and obscene.
The Songs of Bilitis and *The Twilight of the
Nymphs,* banned by the Customs Department.
1930 E.B.Marks of New York was fined $250 for
possessing a copy of *Aphrodite,* in violation of
the State laws against objectionable literature.
1935 The importation of *édition de luxe* copies is now
forbidden, although the above 49 cent copy is
freely advertised in the *New York Times Book
Review,* and is delivered for ten cents extra
through the federal mails.

RASPUTIN, GREGORY. (1871–1916)
My Thoughts and Meditations.
Petrograd, 1915.   (in Russian, first edition)
1915 Russia: In the preface the editors commented
on the author's meteoric rise from lowly peasant
origin. He resented this and forced it to be
deleted from the book.

On Banned Books

SIMKHOVITCH, VLADIMIR G.

Marxism Versus Socialism.

Columbia University Press. New York, 1930, 4th printing. (first edition, 1913)

1917 Russia: The Russian translation was burned at the outbreak of the Revolution. It is now unprocurable; but the volume is available in French, German, Italian, English, and Japanese.

LENIN, VLADIMIR ILYICH ULYANOF.

(1870–1924)

The State and the Revolution.

G.Allen and Unwin. London, 1917.

(first translation from first edition, Russia, 1917)

1927 United States-Boston: Seized as obscene.

Hungary: Seized as subversive.

1928 Canada: *Proletarian Revolution in Russia* burned by the authorities.

TROTSKY, LEON. (Bronstein, Leo) (1880–)

The History of the Russian Revolution.

Translated by Max Eastman.

Simon and Schuster. New York, 1932.

(written, 1930)

1933 Germany: All works banned.

Russia: All works banned.

1934 Italy: All works banned except in *éditions de luxe.*

DREISER, THEODORE. (1871–)

An American Tragedy.

Boni and Liveright. New York, 1925.

(first edition)

1900 United States-Boston: The publication of *Sister*

Carrie incited so much comment that the book
was withdrawn and later corrected.

1916 New York: *The Genius* was suppressed.

1923 *The Genius* was republished; the jacket blurb
flaunted the fact that the volume had been suppressed by the New York Society for the Pre-
vention of Vice.

1930 Boston: The Superior Court condemned *An
American Tragedy* and fined the publisher $300;
but, across the River Charles, it was required
reading for a Harvard English course.

1932 Ireland: *Dawn* banned.

1933 Germany: *The Genius* and *An American Tragedy*
were burned by the Nazis because "they deal
with low love affairs."

1935 United States-Boston: *An American Tragedy*
still banned, though receivable by mail.

SINCLAIR, UPTON. (1878–)
Oil.

Grosset and Dunlap. New York, 1927. (first edition)

1910 United States: A campaign was started to ban
The Jungle, but was unsuccessful.

1929 Yugoslavia: All works banned by the public
libraries.

1930 United States-Boston: *Oil* was forbidden because of comments on the Harding administration. The author defended the case himself and
addressed a crowd of 2,000 on Boston Common
on the character and aim of his book. The nine
pages objected to, including the two pages
quoted from the *Song of Solomon*, were deleted
by a large black fig leaf. The bookseller was
fined $100, and the trial cost the author $2,000.

1933 Germany: Works burned in the Nazi bonfires.

On Banned Books

FEUCHTWANGER, LION. (1884–)
Power.
Translated by Willa and Edwin Muir.
The Modern Library. New York, 1932.
(first edition, 1926)
1914–19 Germany: Works constantly suppressed during the war.
1930 United States-Boston: *Power*, a translation of Aristophanes' *Peace*, was banned for immorality.
1933 Germany: All works burned in the Nazi bonfires. The author was exiled and his property confiscated.

LA MOTTE, ELLEN M. (1873–)
The Backwash of War.
G.P.Putnam's. New York, 1934.
(first edition, London, 1919)
1919 England: Suppressed for its pacifistic thesis.

SANGER, MARGARET. (1883–)
Family Limitation.
The Bakunin Press. London, 1920.
(revision of 9th American edition)
1915 United States: Brought to court by the New York Society for the Suppression of Vice.
William Sanger was jailed for thirty days for distributing his wife's pamphlets on birth control.
1923 London: suppressed.
1931 Irish Free State: Pamphlets banned.
Fascist Italy: Pamphlets banned.
Yugoslavia: Banned.

Informal Notes

STOPES, MARIE C. (Erica Fay, Charlotte Charmichael, Mrs. Reginald Gates.) (1880–)
Wise Parenthood.
Introduction by Arnold Bennett.
G.B.Putnam's Sons. London, 1924.
(first edition, 1918)

1918 England: On publication this volume was made a notorious test case.
Canada: Prohibited.

Married Love.
G.B.Putnam's Sons. London, 1918.   (first edition)
1918 England: 700,000 copies sold.
Canada: Prohibited.
1931 United States: Ban raised by Judge Woolsey on this book and on *Contraception*. His decision was: "I cannot imagine a normal mind to which this book would seem to be obscene or immoral within the proper definition of those words, or whose sex impulses would be stirred by reading it . . . instead of being inhospitably received it should, I think, be welcomed within our borders." Irish Free State: All works banned.
England: The Lord Chamberlain refused to license *Vestia* for the London Stage, although it was legally circulated in book form.

DENNETT, MARY WARE.
The Sex Side of Life, an Explanation for Young People.
Published by the author. New York, 1919.
1922 United States: Declared unmailable by the Post Office Department, although it was published four years earlier by the *Medical Review of Reviews*, and was widely used by the Y.M.C.A. and Government hospitals.

66

Author tried and sentenced by jury to 300 days in jail.

1930 Conviction reversed on appeal.

JOYCE, JAMES. (1882–)
Ulysses.
Shakespeare & Company. Paris, 1922. (first edition)

1918 United States: Early instalments, appearing in *The Little Review*, were burned by the Post Office Department.

1922 Ireland: Burned.

1922 Canada: Banned.
England: 499 copies burned by Customs authorities at Folkstone.
United States: 500 copies burned by Post Office Department.

1924 United States: Manuscript sold at auction for $1,975.

1929 England: Banned.

1934 United States: Ban raised by Judge Woolsey in a notable decision: "A rather strong draught . . . emetic, rather than aphrodisiac . . . a sincere and honest book . . . I do not detect anywhere the leer of a sensualist."
Henry Canby says "It's indecency would have appalled Rabelais and frightened Chaucer; but such a book is valuable in a world trying to be sane, trying to save itself by humour or insight from the pervasion of honest instincts and from mental confusion only because of it's new and brilliant technique, and it's passages of undoubted genius." This book has become required reading in the English courses of many universities.

Informal Notes

CABELL, JAMES BRANCH. (1879–)
Jurgen, A Comedy of Justice.
Robert M. McBride and Company. New York, 1919.
                                                    (first edition)
1920 United States: Prosecuted by the New York
   Society for the Suppression of Vice. This publicity established a hitherto obscure author as a
   best seller.
1922 Although indicted as obscene two years before,
   the book now dismissed as a "work of art."
1935 Volume unobtainable in many large public
   libraries.

LAWRENCE, DAVID HERBERT. (1885–1930)
The Paintings of D.H.Lawrence.
The Mandrake Press. For Subscribers only.
London, 1929.   (first edition)
1922 United States: *Women in Love* seized by John
   S. Sumner of the New York Society for the Suppression of Vice. The case was dismissed in
   court; but the counter suit for libel was sustained.
1929 *Lady Chatterly's Lover* and *Collected Paintings*
   were barred by the customs.
1929 England: *The Rainbow*, freely circulated in
   America, was banned, while *Women in Love* was
   not objected to.
1930 Washington, D.C.: *Lady Chatterly's Lover* had
   prominence in the famed "Decency Debates" in
   the Senate between Senator Bronson Cutting,
   from New Mexico, who was in favor of modifying
   the censorship laws, and Senator Reed Smoot, of
   Utah, who was against it. Cutting enraged Smoot
   by witty insinuations that *Lady Chatterly* was a
   favorite with the Mormon Senator.

On Banned Books

1932 Ireland: *Lady Chatterly's Lover* banned.
Poland: *Lady Chatterly's Lover* banned.

ANDERSON, SHERWOOD. (1876–)
Many Marriages.
Viking Press. New York, 1922.   (first edition)
1923 England: Legal action was aroused and America
laughed.
1930 United States-Boston: *Dark Laughter* was put on
the black list though published five years earlier.
1931 Ireland: *Horses and Men* banned, though published in 1923.

SCHNITZLER, ARTHUR. (1862–)
Casanova's Homecoming.
Simon and Schuster. New York, 1930.
(first German ed., 1918—first American ed., 1921)
1924 United States: The English translation was
indicted as obscene. the indictment was attacked, whereupon Judge Wagner (now Senator)
maintained that the book was sufficiently corrupting for the indictment to stand, his point
being: "We may assert with pride, though not
boastfully, that we are essentially an idealistic
and spiritual nation, and exact a higher standard
than some others." The publisher withheld publication and the case was not tried. Meanwhile
the book circulated freely in the original German.
1930 John S. Sumner brought Simon and Schuster to
court for publishing this volume. The case was
dismissed. *Reigen* (*Hands Around*) was banned
by the Court of Appeals, and the Albany Court
adjudged the book indecent, although it had
been played abroad since 1920.

Informal Notes

DARWIN, CHARLES ROBERT. (1809–1882)
*On the Origin of Species by Means of Natural Selection,
or the Preservation of Favoured Races in the Struggle
for Life.*
John Murray. London, 1859.   (first edition)
1925 Yugoslavia: Prohibited.

> United States: Disapproved of in Tennessee, at
> the scene of the notorious and picturesque trial
> of Scopes, the heretical teacher of Darwin's
> theory of evolution.

ASBURY, HERBERT. (1891–)
Hatrack.
The American Mercury, A Monthly Review edited by
H.L.Mencken. VOL. 7, April, 1926.
Alfred A. Knopf. New York, 1926.
1926 United States-Boston: The New England Watch
> and Ward Society brought the publisher and
> editor of *The American Mercury* into court for
> *Hatrack*, the story of a prostitute. The author
> was unmolested, the editor, Mencken, was ac-
> quitted in court; but a bookseller in Cambridge
> was fined $100 for selling it.

MARKS, PERCY. (1891–)
The Plastic Age.
The Century Company. New York, 1924.
     (first edition)
1927 United States-Boston: Banned for revealing
> casual standards of college life.

On Banned Books

LEWIS, SINCLAIR. (1885–)
Elmer Gantry.
Harcourt, Brace and Company. New York, 1927.

(first edition)

1927 United States-Boston: Banned because a religious hero was depicted as obscene. The publishers defended the suit and expressed their amazement at the discretionary powers invested in local officials. Washington retaliated by upholding postmasters as censors.

1927 Banned by the libraries of St. Louis, Mo., Camden, New Jersey, and Glasgow, Scotland.

1931 Ireland: Banned as offending to public morals. New York: The Post Office Department banned any catalogue listing the book.

DELMAR, VIÑA. (1905–)
Bad Girl.
Harcourt, Brace and Company. New York, 1928.

(first edition)

1928 United States-Boston: Banned by the Watch and Ward Society, although the Literary Guild of America had selected it as their Book of the Month.

1928 Again banned.

1933 Ireland: Prohibited for describing too graphically an illegal abortion.

FORD, HENRY. (1863–)
My Life and Work. Written in collaboration with Samuel Crowther.
Doubleday, Page. 1922.   (first edition)
1927 Russia: Banned.

Informal Notes

DOYLE, CONAN. (1859–1930)
The Adventures of Sherlock Holmes.
Harper Brothers. New York, 1892.

(first American edition)

1929 Russia: Banned because of occultism and spiritualism.

LONDON, JACK. (1876–1916)
The Call of the Wild.
Grosset and Dunlap. New York, 1921.

(first edition, 1903)

1929 Italy: All cheap editions banned.
1929 Jugoslavia: All works banned as too radical.
1932 Germany: Various works were cast into the Nazi bonfires.

HEMINGWAY, ERNEST. (1898–)
A Farewell to Arms.
Charles Scribner's Sons. New York, 1929.

(first edition)

1929 Italy: Banned because of the painfully accurate account of the Italian retreat from Caporetto.
United States: The screen version was privately censored through Italian influence.
Boston: Five issues of *Scribner's Magazine* were prohibited because they contained the story.
1930 Boston: *The Sun Also Rises* banned.
1933 Germany: Works burned in the Nazi bonfires.

O'NEILL, EUGENE. (1888–)
Strange Interlude.
Boni and Liveright, New York, 1928. (first edition)
1929 United States-Boston: Mayor Nichols forbade the stage production. The Theatre Guild promptly gave the play, in a suburb outside the

jurisdiction of Boston, and thousands flocked to see it.

REMARQUE, ERICH MARIA. (1898–)
All Quiet on the Western Front.
Translated from the German by A.W.Wheen.
Little, Brown and Company. Boston, 1929.
(first American edition)

1929 United States: Banned in Boston on grounds of obscenity, although it was expurgated at the suggestion of the Book of the Month Club, whose selection it was.

Chicago: Copies of the English translation seized by the Customs Department.

Austria: Soldiers were forbidden to read the book.

Czechoslovakia: Barred from the military libraries by the war department.

1930 Thuringia: Banned.

1931 Germany: Forbidden in the school libraries by the Diet.

1933 Italy: The translation into Italian banned because of anti-war propaganda.

Germany: All works consigned to the Nazi bonfires.

CONNELLY, MARC. (1890–)
The Green Pastures. A Fable Suggested by Roark Bradford's Southern Sketches, Ol' Man Adam and his Chillun.
Illustrated by Robert Edmund Jones.
Farrar and Rinehart. New York, 1930.
(first edition, 1929)

1929 England: The play was forbidden, as the Deity may not be represented on the stage.

United States: Awarded the Pulitzer Prize as the best play of the year.

1933 Norway: Forbidden to be played in the National Theater.

HUXLEY, ALDUS. (1894–)
Antic Hay.
George H Doran and Company. New York, 1923.

(first edition, England, 1923)

1930 United States-Boston: Banned because of obscenity.

Ireland: *Point Counter Point* banned on the ground of "offending public morals."

1932 Ireland: *Brave New World* banned.

DAKIN, EDWARD FRANDEN. (1898–)
Mrs. Eddy, the Biography of a Virginal Mind.
Charles Scribner's Sons. New York, 1930.

(first edition)

1930 United States: Christian Scientists attempted to suppress this biography throughout the country, especially in Boston where stands the First Church of Christ, Scientist, that governs every branch throughout the world. The methods used were a boycott of bookstores which sold it, and a barrage of letters to publishers and booksellers. Twenty years earlier, Christian Science authorities had bought and destroyed the plates of a biography of Mrs. Eddy by Georgine Milmine.

DODGSON, CHARLES L. (Lewis Carroll).
(1832–1898)
Alice's Adventures in Wonderland.
With 42 illustrations by John Tenniel.
Macmillan and Company. London, 1866.

(second edition)

1931 China: Banned by the Governor of Hunan Province on the ground that "Animals should not use human language, and that it was disastrous to put animals and human beings on the same level."

TOWSLEY, LENA, AND HER CAMERA.
Peggy and Peter, What They Did Today.
Farrar and Rinehart. New York, 1931.

(first and second editions, 1931)

1931 United States-New York: The first edition was printed without the picture of the children saying their prayers at bedtime, as a quasi-intellectual parent did not want the trouble of explaining the picture to her children, who had never heard of God or religion. In recent editions the questionable picture has been included and can be easily torn out, as it is only tipped in.

1930 Russia: The Soviet Government feeling somewhat the same way about the religious question acted similarly. Before the opening of the school season one million copies of a new primary textbook were ready for release. Suddenly a horrified official discovered that in a poem by Nekrasov the word God (Bog) was spelled with a capital letter. To reduce Bog to bog involved changing sixteen pages in each of the million copies; but the change was made, regardless of expense, and the books reached the Soviet children uncontaminated.

DURANT, WILL. (1885–)
The Case for India.
Simon and Schuster. New York, 1930.   (first edition)
1931 England: Banned, with many other pro-Gandhi
    books, by the British Viceroy of India.

HITLER, ADOLF. (1889–)
Mein Kampf.
Franz Ehler. München, 1925–7.   (first edition)
1932 Germany: The authorized translation was considerably deleted for foreign consumption.
1932 Czechoslovakia: Banned for its fierce militaristic doctrines.

LUDWIG, EMIL. (1881–)
Juli 14.
Rowohlt. Berlin, 1929.   (first edition)
1933 Germany-Berlin: All works burned by officers of
    University duelling corps on the grounds of
    "falsifying our history and degrading its great
    figures."

THE BROWN BOOK OF THE HITLER TERROR,
And the Burning of the Reichstag, Prepared by the
World Committee for the Victims of German Fascism.
Introduction by Lord Marley.
Alfred A. Knopf. New York, 1933.   (first edition)
1934 Palestine-Jerusalem: Banned under the ordinance forbidding the defamation of foreign
    princes.

On Banned Books

LE LIVRE DES MILLE NUITS ET UNE NUIT.
Traduction Litérale et complète du texte Arabe par
le Dr. J.C.Mardrus.
Illustrations de Leon Carré; Décoration et Ornements
de Racim Mohammed.
L'Édition D'Art H. Piazza. Paris, 1899.
(first translated into French by A.Galland, 1704–12)
1927 United States-New York: The Customs held up
    500 sets of the translation, by the French
    Scholar, Mardrus, from England.
1931 Ban lifted on the unexpurgated translation from
    the Arabic, by Sir Richard Burton, (1885); but
    the prohibition was maintained on the Mardrus-
    Mather edition.

ARISTOPHANES. (c.444–c.380 b.c.)
Lysistrata.
Illustrated by Norman Lindsey.
Franfrolico Press. London, 1926.
              (written, c.411 b.c.)
1930 United States: Customs ban lifted. During the
    period of prohibition the book was published and
    sold for as little as thirty-five cents; and the
    drama was played in New York and Philadelphia,
    as adapted by Gilbert Seldes.

APULEIUS, LUCIUS. (b.c.a.d.114)
De Asino Auree.
Henricum De Sancto Urso. Vicenza, 1488.
1931 United States: Import ban raised on this book
    which had been freely circulated in the Modern
    Library edition since 1928.

Informal Notes

MICHELANGELO, (Michelangelo Buonarroti).
(1475–1564)
The Last Judgement. M.Boyer D'Agne's Articles on this Masterpiece, and Explanations of the Plates contained in this Book.
Printed in France. n.d.

1933 United States: Plate forty is a copy of *The Last Judgement*, made by Venusti from the original fresco in the Sistine Chapel, before the addition of clothing to the nude figures by Daniele Volterra, by order of Pope Paul IV, and with the permission of Michael Angelo. This book was ordered from Europe by the Weyhe Gallery and Book Shop. They received the following official letter from an assistant collector of customs who, apparently, had never heard of the great painter.

> Sirs:—There is being detained . . . 2 packages addressed to you, containing obscene photo books, 'Ceiling Sistine Chapel,' Filles-Michael Angelo, the importation of which is held to be prohibited under the provisions of the Tariff Act. The package will therefore be seized and disposed of in due course as provided by law. You may however avail yourself of the privilege of applying to the Secretary of the Treasury . . . for mitigation of the penalty of forfeiture with permission to export, or please execute the Assent to forfeiture below, returning same . . . Respectfully, H.C.Stuart, Ass. Collector.

After being ridiculed by the newspapers, the Treasury Department realized the ignorant mistake and relinquished the book.

On Banned Books

LADY MACBETH OF MENSK.

Philadelphia Daily News. Saturday, April 6th, 1935.

1935 United States-Philadelphia: Some obscene trombone notes so shocked certain ladies at the opening night of Shostakovitch's opera that a large number walked out. As the first trombone player refused to play the notes a substitute did so.

Russia-Moscow: "A capacity audience, including Americans, made demonstrations on the rise of each curtain . . . The Opera seems destined to become the first Soviet Classic . . . The music is considered here rich in dramatic and social-psychological content. The foreign audience was deeply impressed."

A GRAPHIC and important part of the exhibit was a large collection of Russian papers from the time of the "Little Revolution" of 1902, the precursor to the Soviet struggle for existence. During this first revolution many revolutionary papers were started, lived precariously through two, five, six issues, only to be stifled by the harsh and ubiquitous Imperial censorship. Entitled diversely, *Machine Gun*, *Woodpecker*, *Whirlpool*, *Dawn*, *Storm*, *Scarecrow*, *Factory Whistle*, etc., these publications have one color in common: blood-red; one theses in common: the devestating abuses perpetrated by a blood-thirsty, spendthrift autocracy on a down-trodden people. Needless to say, all the papers were suppressed.

Perhaps the most elequent of the cartoons is a facsimile of the *Imperial Manifesto* announcing the establishment of a Parliament. The heading reads: "We, Nicholas II, Emperor and Autocrat of all the Russias, King of Poland, Grand Duke of Finland, etc." The printed signature is "Nicholas;" but, as every Imperial decree had to be countersigned by a government official, this manifesto was countersigned by the most hated and feared of all, Major General Trepoff, Chief of Imperial Police. Consequently the people knew that the manifesto was a meaningless sop. In Russian, to countersign is to "put the hand to," and, therefore, the cartoonist has substituted for Trepoff's countersignature his handprint, dipped in the blood of the people.

Another sardonic humorist pictured the revolutionist's dream, and entitled it "Hurried Departure on the River Neva." Nicholas II, his face aghast, has been tumbled unceremoniously on to a swift-moving ice floe, with him his trappings of royalty, symbols of Russian oppression: ermine robe, throne, crown, orb, ikons, imperial eagles, and the very Kremlin itself. From the river bank, Franz Joseph, Abdul Hamid, Ferdinand of Bulgaria, and even Edward VII, look on in dismay.

Again, Nicholas has been portrayed reading the dull official journal, oblivious to the red rats gnawing away the foundations of his throne, and the Kossaks rioting in the streets. Internal evidence of the Czar's censorship appeared in the second issue of a magazine called *Factory Whistle* which had a small reproduction of the frontispiece on the back cover, and the caption, "No. I of *Factory Whistle*, was confiscated; the frontispiece is here in miniature." No. I was also shown in the exhibition.

NAZI BANNED BOOKS

On May 10, 1933, students gathered 25,000 volumes by Jewish authors and burned them in the square in front of the University of Berlin. The bonfire was watched by 40,000 unenthusiastic people in a drizzling rain. Dr. Goebbels, the Minister of Public Enlightenment, delivered an address on "the symbolic significance of the gesture." Similar demonstrations were held at many other German Universities. In Munich 5,000 school children, who had formally seen Markist literature publicly burned, were enjoined; "as you watch the fire burn these un-German books, let it also burn into your hearts love of the Fatherland." Students entered the bookstores and took without remuneration the books they considered eligible for the bonfire, and had to be prevented from confiscating books from the University Library.

In February 1935, an American Library of Nazi banned books, composed entirely of writings banned from Germany by Adolf Hitler, was formally opened at the Jewish Center in Brooklyn by Professor Einstein. In his opening address he said that most of the books had been prohibited in Germany "solely because of their human qualities," and that "every community based on hatred and emnity is predestined to decay because once the negative impulses of the human soul are strongly formed they will of necessity burst forth in daily life."

The following list consists of some of the most important authors whose works were sacrificed at these fires, and whose writings have been shown at this exhibition.

Sholom Asch	Maxim Gorki
Lion Feuchtwanger	Stefan Zweig

Informal Notes

Karl Marx	Franz Werfel
Sigmund Freud	Hugo Munsterberg
Helen Keller	Thomas Mann
Jack London	Heinrich Mann
Ernest Hemingway	Erich Maria Remarque
John Dos Passos	Albert Einstein
Jakob Wasserman	Heinrich Heine
Emil Ludwig	Felix Mendelssohn
Arthur Schnitzler	Maximilian Harden
Leon Trotsky	Kurt Eisner
Nikolai Lenin	Henri Barbusse
Josef Stalin	Rosa Luxemburg
Gregory S.Zinoviev	Upton Sinclair
Alfred Adler	Judge Ben Lindsay
Theodore Lessing	Arnold Zweig

BIBLIOGRAPHIC CHECK LIST

American Book Collector: "Juvenile Literature." 1934.

Bell, Clive. *On British Freedom.* 1923.

Bethléem, L'Abbé Louis. *Romans à Lire et Romans à Proscriere de Classification au Point D'une Moral des Principaux, Romans et Romanciers de Notre Époque.* 1800–1820.

Bowerman, G.T. *Censorship and the Public Library.* 1931.

Bostwick, Arthur E. *The American Public Library.* 1923.

Bowman, J.C. (Editor). *Contemporary American Criticism.* 1926.

Broun, Heywood and Leech, Margaret. *Anthony Comstock: Roundsman of the Lord.* 1927.

Bury, J.B. *History of Freedom of Thought.* 1913.

Canby, Henry S. *Definitions.* 2nd. Series, 1924.

Chaffee, Zechariah, Jr. *Freedom of Speech.* 1920.

Coffin, Victor. "Censorship and Literature under Napoleon I," *The American Historical Review.* 1917.

Congressional Digest: "Censorship of Foreign Books." n.d.

Courtney, Janet. *Free Thinkers of the Nineteenth Century.* 1920.

De Voto, Bernard. *Literary Censorship in Cambridge.* 1931.

Ditchfield, P.H. *Books Fatal To Their Authors.* 1895.

Dreiser, Theodore. *The Meddlesome Decade.* n.d.

Encyclopaedia Britanica. 1912.

Ernst, Morris and Lindey, Alexander: *The Censor Marches On.* M.S. To be published, 1936.

Ernst, Morris and Seagle, William. *To the Pure.* 1929.

Erskine, John. *The Literary Discipline.* 1923.

Informal Notes

Farrar, James Anson. *Books Condemned to be Burned.* 1892.

Fowell, Frank and Palmer, Frank. *Censorship in England.* 1913.

Ford, John. *Criminal Obscenity.* 1926.

Forsyth, William. *Novels and Novelists of the Eighteenth Century.* 1871.

Gillett, Charles Ripley. *Burned Books.* 1932.

Goodrich, Luther Carrington. *The Literary Inquisition of Ch'en-sung.* 1935.

Green, Frederick. *Eighteenth Century France.* n.d.

Gosse, Edmund. "The Censorship of Books," *The Living Age.* 1910.

Graves, Robert. *Lars Porsena, or the Future of Swearing and Improper Language.* 1927.

Hadley, Edwin Marshall. *Sinister Shadows.* 1929.

Hamel, Frank. *English Books in the Indexes.* 1910.

Hart, William H. *Index Expurgatorius Anglicanus. 1523–1681.* 1872-8.

Harvey, Sir Paul. *The Oxford Companion to English Literature.* 1932.

Hays, Arthur Garfield. *Let Freedom Ring.* 1928.

Houben, H.H. *Verbotene Literatur von der Klassischen Zeit bis zur Gegenwart.* 1924.

Howells, William Dean. *Criticism and Fiction.* 1891.

Index Librorum Prohibitorum. 1930.

Index Librorum Prohibitorum. Pro Universius Hispaniarum. n.d.

Kallen, Horace. *Freedom in the Modern World.* 1928.

Krutch, Joseph Wood. *Comedy and Conscience after the Restoration.* 1924.

Lang, Andrew. *The Evolution of Literary Decency.* 1900.

Lecky, W.E.H. *History of the Rise and Influence of the Spirit of Rationalism in Europe.* 1914.

Check List

McDowall, A.S. *Thomas Hardy.* 1931.

Mencken, H.L. *A Book of Prefaces.* 1917.

Mendham, Joseph. *Literary Policy of the Church of Rome.* 1830.

Milton, John. *Areopagitica.* 1644.

Moore, George. "Apologia Pro Scriptis Meis," *Fortnightly Review.* n.d.

New York Public Library Bulletin, Nov. 1934. "Censorship of Foreign Books in Russia under Nicholas I." By Avrahm Yarmolinsky, Ph.D.

Peiquot, G. *Dictionnaire de Livres Condamnés au Feu.* 1806.

Pernicone, Joseph. *The Ecclesiastical Prohibition of Books.* 1932.

Perry, Bliss. *Pernicious Books.* 1924.

Popper, W. *The Censorship of Hebrew Books.* 1899.

Prado, D.D. *Francisci Perez de. Supremi Prasidis, & in Hispaniarum, ac Indiarum Reginis Inquisitorus Generalis Jussa Noviter Auctus, etc.* 1747.

Putnam, George Haven. *The Censorship of the Church of Rome.* 1906.

Putnam, George Haven. *Authors and their Public in Ancient Times.* 1923.

Putnam, George P. (Editor). *Noncensorship.* 1922.

Reusch, Heinrich. *Der Index der Verbotenen Bücher.* 1885.

Richards, I.A. *Principles of Literary Criticism.* 1924.

Rogers, Lindsay. *The Postal Powers of Congress.* 1916.

Rosenbert, James. *Censorship in the United States.* 1928.

Routledge, James. *Freedom of the Press and Trial by Jury.* n.d.

Russell, Phillipps. *Benjamin Franklin, First Civilized American.* 1926.

Schroeder, Theodore. *Free Press Anthology.* 1909.

Informal Notes

Searle, G.M. *Plain Facts for Fair Minds.* 1931.

Shaw, G.B. *The Showing Up of Blanco Posnet, Preface on Censorship.* 1909.

Sherman, Stuart P. *Points of View.* 1924.

Slavonic Review: "Index of the Soviet Inquisition." 1926.

Summers, Montague. *History of Witchcraft and Demonology.* 1926.

Tennyson, Charles. *"The Libraries' Censorship"* in the Contemporary Review. n.d.

Thompson, Albert. *The Controversy Between the Puritans and the Stage.* n.d.

Townley, James. *Illustrations of Biblical Literature.* n.d.

Twain, Mark. *Autobiography.* 1924.

Vickers, R.H. *Martyrdoms of Literature.* n.d.

Vizetelly, Ernst. *Emile Zola, Novelist and Reformer.* 1904.

Weeks, Edward. "The Practice of Censorship." *Atlantic Monthly.* Jan. 1930.

Whipple, Leon. *Story of Civil Liberty in the United States.* 1927.

Young, Kimball. *Bibliography on Censorship and Propaganda.* n.d.

Zevaès, Alexandre. *Les Procès Littéraires au XIXe Siécle.* 1924.

REPORTS, PAMPHLETS, BLACKLISTS

American Civil Liberties Union: "Post Office Censor." 1932. "Repeal the Special Police Powers of the New York Vice Society," etc. 1931.

Brooklyn Jewish Center Review: "Nazi Bonfire List." 1935.

Civil Liberties Committee of Massachusetts: "The Censorship in Boston." 1929.

Check List

Censorship Files from *The New York Times, Time Magazine,* and *Publishers' Weekly.*

Customs Lists from Irish Free State. 1935.

Customs List from Yugoslavia. 1935.

Customs List from The United States. 1928-9.

INDEX

A

Abélard, Pierre, 6

Abridged History of England from the Invasion of Julius Caesar to the Death of George II, 43

Adam Bede, 54

Addison, Joseph, 31

Address to the German Nobility, 12

Advancement of Learning, 23

Adventures of Hucklebury Finn, 53

Adventures of Sherlock Holmes, 72

Adventures of the Black Girl in her Search for God, 60

Adventures of Tom Sawyer, 53

Advice to the Privileged Orders, 39

Aeventyr og Historier, 44

Age of Reason, 40

Agrippa, Henry Cornelius, 10

Alastor, 42

Alice's Adventures in Wonderland, 75

All Quiet on the Western Front, 73

American Mercury, The, Vol. 7, 70

American Tragedy, An, 63

Amor Conjugalis, 32

Amores, 3

Analects, 3

Anderson, Hans Christian, 44

Anderson, Sherwood, 69

Antic Hay, 74

Aphrodite, 62

Appollinaire, Guillaume, 61

Apuleius, Lucius, 77

Areopagitica, A Speech for the Liberty of Unlicenc'd Printing, to the Parliament of England, 24

Aristophanes, 77

Ars Amatoria, 4

Art of Love and other Poems, 3

Asbury, Herbert, 70

Atalie, 42

Aurora Leigh, 54

Avis au Peuple Français, 40

Informal Notes

Index

Informal Notes

Index

Informal Notes

Index

Informal Notes

Index

Informal Notes

Index

Informal Notes

Index

This edition, limited to 1,000 *copies, has been printed at the Morrill Press, Fulton and New York City.*

Typography by Frederic Warde